AMERICAN BOOK COMPANY'S

PASSING THE GEORGIA
ALGEBRA I
END-OF-COURSE TEST

ERICA DAY

ALAN FUQUA

COLLEEN PINTOZZI

AMERICAN BOOK COMPANY

P. O. BOX 2638

WOODSTOCK, GEORGIA 30188-1383

TOLL FREE 1 (888) 264-5877 PHONE (770) 928-2834

FAX (770) 928-7483

WEB SITE: www.americanbookcompany.com

Acknowledgements

In preparing this book, we would like to acknowledge Mary Stoddard and Eric Field for their contributions in editing and developing graphics for this book. We would also like to thank our many students whose needs and questions inspired us to write this text.

Contents

Acknowledgements   ii

Preface   viii

Diagnostic Test   1
    Part 1   1
    Part 2   8

1 Numbers and Number Systems   **16**
  1.1   Real Numbers   16
  1.2   Integers   17
  1.3   Absolute Value   17
  1.4   Multiplying and Dividing Absolute Values   18
  1.5   Order of Operations   18
  1.6   Estimated Solutions   21
  1.7   Understanding Exponents   23
  1.8   Multiplication with Exponents   24
  1.9   Division with Exponents   25
  1.10 Square Root   26
  1.11 Adding and Subtracting Roots   26
  1.12 Multiplying Roots   27
  1.13 Dividing Roots   28
  1.14 Estimating Square Roots   29
  1.15 Properties of Addition and Multiplication 30
       Chapter 1 Review   31

2 Fractions, Decimals, and Percents   **32**
  2.1   Adding Fractions   32
  2.2   Multiplying Fractions   33
  2.3   Dividing Fractions   34
  2.4   Comparing the Relative Magnitude of Fractions   34
  2.5   Changing Fractions to Decimals   35
  2.6   Changing Percents to Decimals and Decimals to Percents   36
  2.7   Changing Percents to Fractions and Fractions to Percents   37
  2.8   Comparing the Relative Magnitude of Numbers   38
       Chapter 2 Review   40

3 Introduction to Graphing — **41**

3.1 Graphing on a Number Line — 41

3.2 Graphing Fractional Values — 41

3.3 Recognizing Improper Fractions, Decimals, and Square Root Values on a Number Line — 43

3.4 Plotting Points on a Vertical Number Line — 45

3.5 Cartesian Coordinates — 46

3.6 Identifying Ordered Pairs — 47

Chapter 3 Review — 49

4 Introduction to Algebra — **50**

4.1 Algebra Vocabulary — 50

4.2 Substituting Numbers for Variables — 51

4.3 Understanding Algebra Word Problems — 52

4.4 Setting Up Algebra Word Problems — 54

4.5 Changing Algebra Word Problems to Algebraic Equations — 55

Chapter 4 Review — 56

5 Ratios and Proportions — **58**

5.1 Ratio Problems — 58

5.2 Solving Proportions — 58

5.3 Ratio and Proportion Word Problems — 59

5.4 Direct and Indirect Variation — 61

Chapter 5 Review — 63

6 Solving One-Step Equations and Inequalities — **64**

6.1 One-Step Algebra Problems With Addition and Subtraction — 64

6.2 One-Step Algebra Problems With Multiplication and Division — 65

6.3 Multiplying and Dividing With Negative Numbers — 66

6.4 Variables With A Coefficient of Negative One — 67

6.5 Graphing Inequalities — 68

6.6 Solving Inequalities by Addition and Subtraction — 69

6.7 Solving Inequalities by Multiplication and Division — 70

Chapter 6 Review — 71

7 Solving Multi-Step Equations and Inequalities — **73**

7.1 Two-Step Algebra Problems — 73

7.2 Two-Step Algebra Problems With Fractions — 74

Contents

7.3	More Two-Step Algebra Problems With Fractions	75
7.4	Rationalizing the Denominator	76
7.5	Combining Like Terms	76
7.6	Solving Equations With Like Terms	77
7.7	Multi-Step Algebra Problems	79
7.8	Solving Radical Equations	81
7.9	Multi-Step Inequalities	82
7.10	Solving Equations and Inequalities with Absolute Values	84
7.11	More Solving Equations and Inequalities with Absolute Values	85
	Chapter 7 Review	87

8 Polynomials — **88**

8.1	Adding and Subtracting Monomials	88
8.2	Adding Polynomials	89
8.3	Subtracting Polynomials	90
8.4	Multiplying Monomials	91
8.5	Multiplying Monomials by Polynomials	92
8.6	Dividing Polynomials by Monomials	93
8.7	Removing Parentheses and Simplifying	94
8.8	Multiplying Two Binomials	95
8.9	Simplifying Expressions with Exponents	96
	Chapter 8 Review	97

9 Factoring — **98**

9.1	Factor By Grouping	101
9.2	Factoring Trinomials	102
9.3	More Factoring Trinomials	103
9.4	Factoring More Trinomials	104
9.5	Factoring Trinomials With Two Variables	105
9.6	Factoring the Difference of Two Squares	106
	Chapter 9 Review	109

10 Solving Quadratic Equations — **110**

10.1	Solving the Difference of Two Squares	112
10.2	Solving Perfect Squares	114
10.3	Completing the Square	115
10.4	Using the Quadratic Formula	116
10.5	Pythagorean Theorem	117

10.6	Finding the Missing Leg of a Right Triangle	118
	Chapter 10 Review	119

11 Graphing and Writing Equations and Inequalities   **120**

11.1	Graphing Linear Equations	120
11.2	Graphing Horizontal and Vertical Lines	122
11.3	Finding the Intercepts of a Line	123
11.4	Understanding Slope	124
11.5	Slope-Intercept Form of a Line	126
11.6	Verify That a Point Lies On a Line	127
11.7	Graphing a Line Knowing a Point And Slope	128
11.8	Finding the Equation of a Line Using Two Points or a Point and Slope	129
11.9	Changing the Slope or Y-Intercept of a Line	130
11.10	Equations of Perpendicular Lines	132
11.11	Writing an Equation From Data	134
11.12	Graphing Linear Data	135
11.13	Identifying Graphs of Linear Equations	138
11.14	Graphing Non-Linear Equations	139
11.15	Graphing Inequalities	140
	Chapter 11 Review	143

12 Systems of Equations and Systems of Inequalities   **146**

12.1	Finding Common Solutions for Intersecting Lines	147
12.2	Solving Systems of Equations by Substitution	148
12.3	Solving Systems of Equations by Adding or Subtracting	150
12.4	Graphing Systems of Inequalities	152
	Chapter 12 Review	153

13 Relations and Functions   **154**

13.1	Relations	154
13.2	Determining Domain and Range From Graphs	155
13.3	Functions	158
13.4	Recognizing Functions	159
	Chapter 13 Review	162

14 Statistics   **163**

14.1	Range	163
14.2	Mean	164

Contents

14.3   Finding Data Missing From the Mean   165

14.4   Median   166

14.5   Mode   167

14.6   Scatter Plots   168

14.7   The Line of Best Fit   170

       Chapter 14 Review   171

15 Probability   **173**

15.1   Compound Independent Events   175

15.2   More Probability   177

       Chapter 15 Review   178

Practice Test 1   **181**

       Part 1   181

       Part 2   188

Practice Test 2   **195**

       Part 1   195

       Part 2   202

Index   **207**

Preface

Passing the Georgia Algebra I End-of-Course Test will help you review and learn important concepts and skills related to Algebra I. Some of this material will be a review of skills you have already learned, while other sections will present you with new applications in Arithmetic, Algebra, Graphing, Statistics, and Probability. To help identify which areas are greater challenges for you, complete the evaluation chart with your instructor in order to help you identify the chapters which require your careful attention. When you have finished your review of all of the material your teacher assigns, take the practice tests to evaluate your understanding of the material presented in this book. **The materials in this book are based on the standards and content descriptions for mathematics published by the Georgia Department of Education.**

This book contains several sections: 1) A Diagnostic Test; 2) Chapters that teach the concepts and skills for *Passing the Georgia Algebra I End-of-Course Test*; 3) Two Practice Tests. Answers to the tests and exercises are in a separate manual.

The Diagnostic and Practice Tests are divided into the following topics:

Domain	Number of Questions
Algebraic Fundamentals	18
Operations on Real Numbers and Algebraic Expressions	18
Solving Equations and Inequalities	18
Functions and Their Graphs	18
Connections and Applications	18
Total # of Questions	**90**

We welcome comments and suggestions about the book. Please contact the authors at

American Book Company

P.O. Box 2638

Woodstock, GA 30188-1383

Toll Free 1 (888) 264-5877

Phone (770) 928-2834

Fax (770) 928-7483

Web site: www.americanbookcompany.com

ABOUT THE AUTHORS

Erica Day is working on a Bachelor of Science Degree in Mathematics at Kennesaw State University, Kennesaw, GA. She is a senior and has been on the Dean's List for her entire undergraduate career. She has also tutored all levels of mathematics, ranging from high school algebra and geometry to university-level statistics and linear algebra. She is currently participating in a mathematics internship for American Book Company, where she does writing and editing.

Alan Fuqua graduated from the Georgia Institute of Technology with a Bachelor of Chemical Engineering degree. He has over fifteen years of industrial experience in the manufacture of inorganic chemicals, including implementing lean manufacturing principles and training employees. He has extensive experience applying statistical models and Six Sigma principles to process improvement and cost savings. He is currently the Mathematics Coordinator for the American Book Company and is continuing his Mathematics education at Kennesaw State University.

Colleen Pintozzi has taught mathematics at the middle school, junior high, senior high, and adult level for 22 years. She hold a B.S. degree from Wright State University in Dayton, Ohio and has done graduate work at Wright State University, Duke University, and the University of North Carolina at Chapel Hill. She is the author of eight mathematics books including such best-sellers as **Basics Made Easy: Mathematics Review, Passing the New Alabama Graduation Exam in Mathematics, Passing the Georgia High School Graduation Test in Mathematics, Writing, and English Language Arts, Passing the TCAP Competency Test in Mathematics, Passing the Louisiana LEAP 21 Graduation Exit Exam, Passing the Indiana ISTEP+ Graduation Qualifying Exam in Mathematics, Passing the Minnesota Basic Standards Test in Mathematics,** and **Passing the Nevada High School Proficiency Exam in Mathematics.**

FORMULA SHEET

distance = rate × time	$d = rt$
Distance Formula:	$d = \sqrt{(x_2-x_1)^2 + (y_2-y_1)^2}$
Point-Slope Equation:	$y - y_1 = m(x - x_1)$
Pythagorean Theorem:	$a^2 + b^2 = c^2$
Slope Formula:	$m = \dfrac{y_2-y_1}{x_2-x_1}$
Slope-Intercept Equation:	$y = mx + b$
$\pi = \text{pi} = 3.14 \text{ or } \dfrac{22}{7}$	

PERIMETER (P) and CIRCUMFERENCE (C)

Any Polygon:	P = sum of side lengths
Rectangle:	$P = 2l + 2w$
Circle:	$C = 2\pi r$ or πd

PLANE FIGURES	AREA (A)
Triangle:	$A = \frac{1}{2}bh$
Rectangle:	$A = lw$
Circle:	$A = \pi r^2$

SOLID FIGURES	VOLUME (V)
Prism:	$V = Bh$ or $V = lwh$
Cube:	$V = s^3$

n	$\sqrt{n}$	n^2
1	1.000	1
2	1.414	4
3	1.732	9
4	2.000	16
5	2.236	25
6	2.449	36
7	2.646	49
8	2.828	64
9	3.000	81
10	3.162	100
11	3.317	121
12	3.464	144
13	3.606	169
14	3.742	196
15	3.873	225
16	4.000	256
17	4.123	289
18	4.243	324
19	4.359	361
20	4.472	400
21	4.583	441
22	4.690	484
23	4.796	529
24	4.899	576
25	5.000	625

ABBREVIATIONS

A = area	l = length
B = area of base	P = perimeter
b = base	r = radius
C = circumference	s = length of side
d = diameter	V = volume
h = height	w = width

Diagnostic Test

Part 1

1. Solve $3x^2 - 12x + 6$ using the quadratic formula.

   (A) $(2, 2 - \sqrt{2})$
   (B) $(3 + \sqrt{2}, 3 - \sqrt{2})$
   (C) $(-3, -\frac{2}{3})$
   (D) $(2 + \sqrt{2}, 2 - \sqrt{2})$

2. $3\frac{2}{5}$ is the same as

   (A) 3.4
   (B) 3.25
   (C) 0.34
   (D) 0.034

3. $\frac{5}{8}$ written as a percent is

   (A) 0.58%
   (B) 0.625%
   (C) 6.25%
   (D) 62.5%

4. A table and chairs set that normally sells for $450.00 is on sale this week for 30% off the regular price. How much money would Trina save if she bought the set this week?

   (A) $30.00
   (B) $31.50
   (C) $135.00
   (D) $315.00

5. Last year, there were 96 students in the marching band. This year, the band's size has increased by 25%. How many students are in the marching band this year?

   (A) 121
   (B) 120
   (C) 24
   (D) 125

6. Cheryl borrows $7,500.00 to buy a used car at 12% simple interest per year. Cheryl makes no payments during the first year. How much interest does she owe at the end of the year?

   (A) $120.00
   (B) $750.00
   (C) $850.00
   (D) $900.00

7. Which of the following is equivalent to 3^{-5}?

   (A) -45
   (B) -15
   (C) $\dfrac{1}{243}$
   (D) 3×10^{-5}

8. Isabella is simplifying this expression:
   $2(5a + 3b - c) - 5(4a - 2b - 3c)$
   The expression above is equivalent to which of the following expressions?

   (A) $-10a + 16b + 13c$
   (B) $-10a - 4b - 4c$
   (C) $30a + b + 2c$
   (D) $30a - 4b - 17c$

1

9. Simplify the expression shown: $\dfrac{8x^4}{2x^2}$

   (A) $2x^4$

   (B) $4x^2$

   (C) $\dfrac{1}{4x^2}$

   (D) $\dfrac{4x^2}{x}$

10. Andrea has 10 more jellybeans than her friend Chelsea, but Andrea has half as many as Rebecca. Which expression below best describes Rebecca's jelly beans?

    (A) $R = 2C + 20$
    (B) $R = C + 10$
    (C) $R = A + \dfrac{1}{2}C$
    (D) $R = 2A + 10$

11. A builder is constructing a fence 85 feet long. Each section of fence contains 6 beams of wood and takes up $2\dfrac{1}{2}$ feet. How many beams of wood will the builder need?

    (A) 102 beams
    (B) 204 beams
    (C) 308 beams
    (D) 420 beams

12. What is the x-intercept of the following linear equation?
    $3x + 4y = 12$

    (A) $(0, 3)$
    (B) $(3, 0)$
    (C) $(0, 4)$
    (D) $(4, 0)$

13. Heather eats 2 cookies with 90 calories each, 1 glass of skim milk with 110 calories, and a sandwich with 212 calories. She thinks she consumed 502 calories. Estimating to the hundreds place, which would verify her calculations?

    (A) $90 + 100 + 200$
    (B) $100 + 100 + 100 + 200$
    (C) $90 + 90 + 110 + 200$
    (D) $180 + 110 + 200$

14. Which of the following equations is represented by the graph?

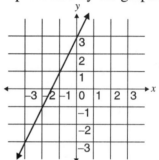

    (A) $y = -3x + 3$
    (B) $y = -\dfrac{1}{3}x + 3$
    (C) $y = 3x - 3$
    (D) $y = 2x + 3$

15. Elise calculates that after Christmas shopping, she will have $30.85 in her checking account. She currently has $212.68 in her account, and she plans on purchasing 12 gift baskets at $15.95 each. Based on the above information,

    (A) Elise has over-calculated the amount in her checking account by about $10.00.
    (B) Elise has under-calculated the amount in her checking account by about $10.00.
    (C) Elise has over-calculated the amount in her checking account by about $30.00.
    (D) Elise has under-calculated the amount in her checking account by about $20.00.

16. Solve: $6 - 2(5y - 1) = 18$

   (A) $y = 2$
   (B) $y = -2$
   (C) $y = 1$
   (D) $y = -1$

17. What is the equation of the line that includes the point $(4, -3)$ and has a slope of -2?

   (A) $y = -2x - 5$
   (B) $y = -2x - 2$
   (C) $y = -2x + 5$
   (D) $y = 2x - 5$

18. Brandi spins the spinner twice. What is the probability that the sum of the two spins is an even number?

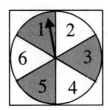

   (A) $\dfrac{1}{2}$

   (B) $\dfrac{1}{12}$

   (C) $\dfrac{1}{6}$

   (D) $\dfrac{1}{3}$

19. Simplify: $\sqrt{45} \times \sqrt{27}$

   (A) $3\sqrt{15}$
   (B) $\sqrt{72}$
   (C) $\sqrt{121}$
   (D) $9\sqrt{15}$

20. Which of the following graphs represents $y = 2x^2$?

   (A)
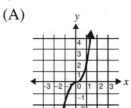

   (B)
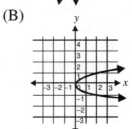

   (C)
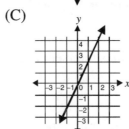

   (D)
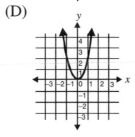

21. $5^{15} \times 5^{-12} =$
   (A) 25
   (B) 125
   (C) 243
   (D) 0.125

22. Solve the following inequality:
   $-3(4x + 5) > (5x + 6) + 13$
   (A) $x < -\frac{14}{17}$
   (B) $x > -2$
   (C) $x > \frac{20}{11}$
   (D) $x < -2$

23. Consider the following equations:
$f(x) = 3x + 2$ and $f(x) = 3x - 7$.
Which of the following statements is true concerning the graphs of these equations?

(A) The graphs of the equations are lines that are perpendicular to each other.

(B) The graph of the line represented by the equation $f(x) = 3x + 2$ always remains above the x-axis, while the graph of the line represented by the equation $f(x) = 3x - 7$ always remains below the x-axis.

(C) The graphs of the equations are lines that are parallel to each other, but that have different y-intercepts.

(D) The graphs of the lines intersect each other at the point $(2, -7)$.

24. What is the solution to the following system of equations?
$y = 4x - 8$
$y = 2x$

(A) $(-4, -8)$
(B) $(4, 8)$
(C) $(-1, -2)$
(D) $(1, 2)$

25. Simplify: $\dfrac{\sqrt{20}}{\sqrt{35}}$

(A) $\dfrac{2\sqrt{7}}{7}$

(B) $\dfrac{2}{\sqrt{7}}$

(C) $\dfrac{2\sqrt{5}}{\sqrt{7}}$

(D) $\dfrac{4}{7}$

26. Simplify the expression shown below:
$3x^{-2}$

(A) $(3x)^{-1}(3x)^{-1}$

(B) $\dfrac{9}{x^2}$

(C) $\dfrac{1}{3x^2}$

(D) $\dfrac{3}{x^2}$

27. Solve for a: $-2(-3 - 5) = 3 - a$

(A) -13
(B) 19
(C) 13
(D) -19

28. Jeff was making $\$6.25$ per hour. His boss gives him a $\$0.75$ per hour raise. What percent raise does Jeff get?

(A) 12%
(B) 25%
(C) 40%
(D) 70%

29. Find c: $\dfrac{c}{-2} > -6$

(A) $c > -12$
(B) $c < 12$
(C) $c > 12$
(D) $c < 3$

30. The regular price of a stereo (r) is $\$560$. The stereo is on sale for 25% off. Which equation will help you find the sale price (s) of the stereo?

(A) $s = r - .25$
(B) $s = r - .25s$
(C) $s = r - .25r$
(D) $s = r - s$

31. $(3x^2 - 5x + 6) - (x^2 + 4x - 7) =$

    (A) $4x^2 - x - 1$
    (B) $4x^2 - x + 13$
    (C) $2x^2 - 9x - 1$
    (D) $2x^2 - 9x + 13$

32. In the following equation, which are the variable, the terms and the coefficient?
$9x - 3 = 78$

    (A) Variable $= x$
        Terms $= 9x, -3$
        Coefficient $= 9$
    (B) Variable $= -3$
        Terms $= 78, -3$
        Coefficient $= -3$
    (C) Variable $= 9$
        Terms $= 9, -3$
        Coefficient $= x$
    (D) Variable $= 78$
        Terms $= 78, 9$
        Coefficient $= x$

33. What is the value of the expression $5(x + 6)$ when $x = -3$?

    (A) -9
    (B) 15
    (C) 9
    (D) 45

34. Find the equation of the line perpendicular to the line containing the points $(-2, -3)$ and $(1, 4)$ and passing through the point $(0, 3)$.

    (A) $y = \dfrac{3}{7}x - 3$

    (B) $y = -\dfrac{3}{7}x + 3$

    (C) $y = -\dfrac{3}{7}x - 3$

    (D) $y = -\dfrac{7}{3}x + 3$

35. An arrow shoots upward with an initial velocity of 128 feet per second. The height (h) of the arrow is a function of time (t) in seconds since the arrow left the ground and can be expressed by the equation $h = 128t - 16t^2$. When will the arrow be at a height of 240 feet?

    (A) At 3 seconds and at 5 seconds
    (B) Only at 3 seconds
    (C) Only at 5 seconds
    (D) Only at 8 seconds

36. $(-a^3 + 2a^2 - 8) - (-4a^3 + 5a - 2) =$

    (A) $3a^3 + 2a^2 - 5a - 6$
    (B) $-5a^3 + 7a^2 - 10$
    (C) $3a^3 + 7a^2 - 6$
    (D) $-5a^3 + 7a^2 - 6$

37. Solve $I = PRT$ for R.

    (A) $R = IPT$
    (B) $R = I + PT$
    (C) $R = I - PT$
    (D) $R = \dfrac{I}{PT}$

38. Which order of operations should be used to simplify the following expression?
$12 \div 2 + 4(7 - 5)$

    (A) subtract, multiply, add, divide
    (B) divide, add, subtract, multiply
    (C) divide, add, multiply, subtract
    (D) subtract, divide, multiply, add

39. Which of the following computations will result in an irrational number?

    (A) 7π

    (B) $3\dfrac{1}{2} + 7\dfrac{1}{4}$

    (C) $6.8 - 3.9$

    (D) $5 - \dfrac{1}{2}$

40. Which table of values below represents a linear function?

(A)
x	y
0	−3
1	−1
2	1

(C)
x	y
0	2
−1	0
−2	−1

(B)
x	y
−1	5
−2	0
1	3

(D)
x	y
2	3
5	7
8	9

41. Which equation matches the following graph?

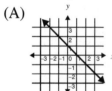

(A) $y = 3x - 2$

(B) $y + 2 = -3x$

(C) $3(y + 2) = 2x$

(D) $2(y + 2) = 3x$

42. What graph shows a line that has a slope of -1 and a y-intercept of $(0, 1)$?

(A)
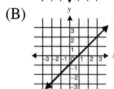

(B)
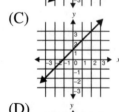

(C)

(D)
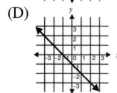

43. Which graph represents a line containing the points $(-2, -3)$ and $(1, 4)$?

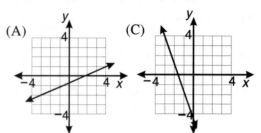

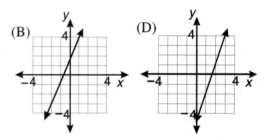

(A)   (C)

(B)   (D)

44. A 25-foot ladder is leaning against a building. The base of the ladder is 7 feet from the base of the building. How high up the building does the ladder reach?

(A) 21 feet

(B) 22 feet

(C) 23 feet

(D) 24 feet

45. Write 3^{-2} as a fraction.

(A) $\dfrac{1}{6}$

(B) $\dfrac{1}{9}$

(C) $\dfrac{2}{3}$

(D) $\dfrac{3}{2}$

6

 If you want to check your answers to Part 1 questions 1–45 or take a five minute break, you may do so now. After you have checked your answers, continue with the rest of the test. On the Georgia Algebra I End-of-Course Test, you will be able to have a five minute break between each part.

Part 2

1. Solve the equation $(x - 4)^2 = 25$

    (A) $x = -4, -5$
    (B) $x = 9, -1$
    (C) $x = 5, -5$
    (D) $x = 4, -4$

2. Sally, Janet and Nancy are helping with a reforestation project. Sally plants between 50 and 90 seedlings per hour. Janet and Nancy each plant between 40 and 75 trees per hour. Which of these inequalities represents the possible range of total number of trees the three workers can plant in one hour?

    (A) $90 \leq x \leq 165$
    (B) $130 \leq x \leq 240$
    (C) $150 \leq x \leq 280$
    (D) $180 \leq x \leq 330$

3. Simplify $2^3 \times 2^5$

    (A) 2
    (B) 2^{-2}
    (C) 2^{15}
    (D) 2^8

4. Simplify $(\sqrt{64})^2$

    (A) 64

    (B) 16

    (C) $\frac{1}{64}$

    (D) $\frac{1}{8}$

5. Which members of the set $\{-3, -2, -1, 0, 1, 2, 3\}$ are solutions for the inequality $-2x + 5 > 10$?

    (A) $\{-3, -2\}$
    (B) $\{0, 1, 2, 3\}$
    (C) $\{-3, -2, -1\}$
    (D) $\{-3\}$

6. $|-8| - |4| =$

    (A) 4
    (B) -4
    (C) 12
    (D) -12

7. Solve the equation $x^2 - 6x + 7 = 0$ by completing the square.

    (A) $x = 7, -1$
    (B) $x = \sqrt{3}, -\sqrt{3}$
    (C) $x = 3 - \sqrt{2}, \sqrt{2} + 3$
    (D) $x = 3 + 2i, 3 - 2i$

8. Solve the equation $x = \sqrt{4x - 3}$

    (A) $x = 1, 3$
    (B) $x = \pm\sqrt{3}$
    (C) $x = -1, -3$
    (D) $x = 2\sqrt{3}, -2\sqrt{3}$

9. What is the intercept of the following linear equations?
    $y = 3x - 1$
    $y = 4x + 2$

    (A) $(-3, 10)$
    (B) $(-3, -10)$
    (C) $(10, -3)$
    (D) $(3, -10)$

10. Evaluate $4x^3 - 2x^2 - 3x + 1$ given $x = -2$.

    (A) 533
    (B) 489
    (C) -33
    (D) 22

11. Fido gets 2 doggy treats every time he sits and 4 doggy treats when he rolls over on command. Throughout the week, he has sat 6 times as often as he has rolled over. In total, he has earned 80 doggy treats. How many times has Fido sat?

(A) 4
(B) 5
(C) 24
(D) 30

12. Which equation does the graph of the line below represent?

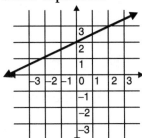

(A) $y = \dfrac{1}{2}x$

(B) $y = \dfrac{1}{2}x - 2$

(C) $y = \dfrac{1}{2}x + 2$

(D) $y = -2x$

13. Solve the following quadratic equation by factoring: $3x^2 = 4x + 7$

(A) $-\dfrac{1}{3}, \dfrac{7}{3}$

(B) $-1, \dfrac{7}{3}$

(C) $-1, -2$

(D) $-\dfrac{7}{3}, \dfrac{3}{7}$

14. Multiply and simplify:
$(3x + 2)(x - 4)$

(A) $3x^2 - 10x - 8$
(B) $3x^2 + 5x - 8$
(C) $3x^2 + 5x - 6$
(D) $8x^2 - 2$

15. Translate the following sentence into an algebraic equation: "Two times the sum of a number, x, and 6 is 14."

(A) $2x + 6 = 14$
(B) $2x - 6 = 14$
(C) $2(x + 6) = 14$
(D) $2(x - 6) = 14$

16. Which of the following is a graph of the inequality $y \le x - 3$?

(A)
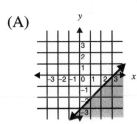

(B)
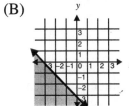

(C)
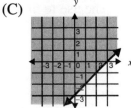

(D)
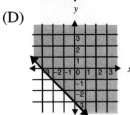

17. Which of these is the best estimate of the coordinate of Point P on the number line?

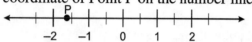

(A) $-1\dfrac{1}{8}$

(B) $-1\dfrac{3}{8}$

(C) $-1\dfrac{5}{8}$

(D) $-2\dfrac{3}{8}$

18. Which point on the number line represents $-2\dfrac{3}{4}$?

(A) P
(B) Q
(C) R
(D) S

19. A recipe for 32 ounces of lemonade calls for 4 ounces of lemon juice. Janet wants to make 120 ounces of lemonade. Which proportion below should she use to find the amount of lemon juice needed?

(A) $\dfrac{32}{120} = \dfrac{x}{4}$

(B) $\dfrac{x}{32} = \dfrac{4}{120}$

(C) $\dfrac{32}{4} = \dfrac{x}{120}$

(D) $\dfrac{4}{32} = \dfrac{x}{120}$

20. In Betty's class there are 16 girls and 14 boys. Which of these is the correct ratio of girls to the total number of students in the class?

(A) 14 to 16
(B) 16 to 14
(C) 14 to 30
(D) 16 to 30

21. Simplify: $12 + (5 \times 2)^2 \times 14$

(A) 152
(B) 1412
(C) 1568
(D) 16,184

22. Which of these is the equation of the line that generalizes the pattern of the data in the table?

x	f(x)
−4	−7
0	1
1	3
6	13

(A) $f(x) = -4 - 7$
(B) $f(x) = x + 2$
(C) $f(x) = 2x + 1$
(D) $f(x) = -7 - 4$

23. Solve: $3(x - 2) - 1 = 6(x + 5)$

(A) -4

(B) $-\dfrac{37}{3}$

(C) 4

(D) $\dfrac{23}{3}$

24. Which of these graphs represents $2x > -3$?

(A)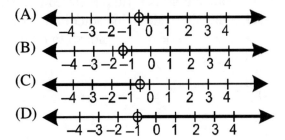

(B)

(C)

(D)

25. Which of these expressions represents the average rate in miles per hour between 7 AM and 11 AM?

Time	Odometer Reading
7 AM	20825
11 AM	20965

(A) $\dfrac{20825 - 20965}{11 - 7}$

(B) $\dfrac{20825 - 7}{20965 - 11}$

(C) $\dfrac{20965 - 11}{20965 - 7}$

(D) $\dfrac{20965 - 20825}{11 - 7}$

26. Susanna is buying at least 150 sodas for the school dance party. She buys 2 cases with 24 sodas in each case. She also buys some six-packs of soda. Determine the number of six-packs Susanna buys using the following inequality.
$6x + 2(24) \geq 150$

(A) $x \geq 17$
(B) $x \geq 20$
(C) $x \geq 21$
(D) $x \geq 25$

27. In the first five games this season, Mike scored the following number of points:
16, 25, 18, 22, 19
What is the mean (average) number of points per game?

(A) 13.6
(B) 16.4
(C) 20
(D) 25

28. Justin measured the heights of 10 basketball players. Their heights, in inches, are given below.

$$71, 82, 72, 78, 73, 76, 72, 75, 73, 78$$

What is the median height of the 10 basketball players?

(A) 73 inches
(B) 74 inches
(C) 75 inches
(D) 76 inches

29. Look at the graphs below. Which of the following statements is false?

(i)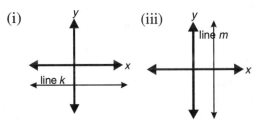

(iii)

(ii)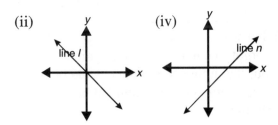

(iv)

(A) The slope of line k is undefined.
(B) The slope of line l is negative.
(C) The slope of line m is undefined.
(D) The slope of line n is positive.

30. The ratio of pine trees to hardwood trees in this park is 5 to 7. What percent of the trees are pine trees?

(A) 71.4%
(B) 41.6%
(C) 58.3%
(D) 57%

31. Find the length of the hypotenuse, h, of the following triangle.

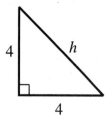

(A) 16
(B) $4\sqrt{2}$
(C) 6
(D) 32

32. Enrique got 79% on his first history test. How much must he get on his second test if he wants an 88% average?

(A) 97%
(B) 96%
(C) 93%
(D) 88%

33. Pat wants to divide 7.86 by 3.9, but he forgot to enter the decimal points when he put the numbers into the calculator. Using estimation, where should Pat put the decimal point?

(A) 0.2015386
(B) 2.015386
(C) 20.15386
(D) 201.5386

34. Rami has an aquarium with 3 black goldfish and 4 orange goldfish. He purchased 2 more black goldfish to add to his aquarium. What is the new ratio of black goldfish to total goldfish?

(A) $\dfrac{2}{9}$

(B) $\dfrac{5}{9}$

(C) $\dfrac{4}{5}$

(D) $\dfrac{5}{4}$

35. Between what two integers does the square root of 7 lie?

(A) 1 and 2
(B) 2 and 3
(C) 3 and 4
(D) 4 and 9

36. Simplify the expression shown below:
$$\dfrac{3^{-3}}{2}$$

(A) $-\dfrac{9}{2}$

(B) $-\dfrac{27}{2}$

(C) $\dfrac{1}{54}$

(D) $\dfrac{1}{216}$

37. Solve the following inequality:
$$-3(4x + 5) > 2(5x + 6) + 13$$

(A) $x < -\dfrac{20}{11}$

(B) $x > 20$

(C) $x > \dfrac{20}{11}$

(D) $x < 20$

38. Assume v is an integer and solve for v.
$12 - 3|v| \geq 6$

(A) $\{-3, -2, -1, 0, 1, 2, 3\}$
(B) $\{-2, -1, 0, 1, 2\}$
(C) $\{-2, -1, 0, 1\}$
(D) $\{-1, 0, 1\}$

39. Which of the following lines is parallel to $y = -4x + 6$?

(A) $y = -2x + 6$
(B) $y = -4x + 2$
(C) $y = 4x + 6$
(D) $y = 2x + 6$

40. The spinner below stopped on the number 5 on the first spin. What is the probability that it will not stop on the number 5 on the second spin?

(A) $\dfrac{1}{5}$

(B) $\dfrac{1}{3}$

(C) $\dfrac{1}{6}$

(D) $\dfrac{5}{6}$

41. Tate is saving his money to buy a go-cart. The go-cart he wants costs $240. His mother agreed to give him $60. What percent of the total cost of the go-cart is his mother contributing?

(A) 20%
(B) 25%
(C) 40%
(D) 75%

42. Rachel keeps track of how many scoops she sells of the five most popular flavors in her ice cream shop.

Flavor	Scoops
Vanilla Bean	30
Chunky Chocolate	36
Strawberry Coconut	44
Chocolate Peanut Butter	46
Mint Chocolate Chip	28

Which flavor of ice cream is closest to the mean number?

(A) Vanilla Bean
(B) Chocolate Peanut Butter
(C) Chunky Chocolate
(D) Strawberry Coconut

43. Which of the following shows the Identity Property of Addition?

(A) $a + 0 = a$
(B) $a + b = b + a$
(C) $a + (-a) = 0$
(D) $a + (b + c) = (a + b) + c$

44. Adam has a bag containing 6 white marbles and 4 black marbles. Bob's marble bag contains 2 white marbles, 4 red marbles, and 3 blue marbles. If Adam and Bob each randomly take one marble from their respective bags, what is the probability that both boys will choose white marbles?

(A) $\dfrac{2}{19}$

(B) $\dfrac{2}{15}$

(C) $\dfrac{12}{30}$

(D) $\dfrac{8}{19}$

45. Based on the information below, what is the relationship between rainfall and water usage?

Daily Rainfall (in)	Daily Household Water Usage (gallons)
0.5	175
3	100
5	90
2	120
4	110
1	160

(A) No relationship

(B) Negative

(C) Positive

(D) Cannot be determined

Evaluation Chart for the Diagnostic Mathematics Test

Directions: On the following chart, circle the question numbers that you answered incorrectly. Then turn to the appropriate topics (listed by chapters), read the explanations, and complete the exercises. Review the other chapters as needed. Finally, complete the *Passing the Georgia Algebra I End-of-Course* Practice Tests to further review.

		Questions - Part 1	Questions - Part 2	Pages
Chapter 1:	Numbers and Number Systems	7, 13, 19, 21, 25, 26, 38, 39, 45	3, 4, 6, 21, 36, 43	16–31
Chapter 2:	Fractions, Decimals, and Percents	2, 3, 4, 5, 6, 11, 15, 28	33, 41	32–40
Chapter 3:	Introduction to Graphing		17, 18, 35	41–49
Chapter 4:	Introduction to Algebra	10, 30, 32, 33	10, 11, 15	50–57
Chapter 5:	Ratios and Proportions		19, 20, 30,34	58–63
Chapter 6:	Solving One-Step Equations and Inequalities	29, 37	2, 24	64–72
Chapter 7:	Solving Multi-Step Equations and Inequalities	16, 22, 27	23, 16, 37, 38	73–87
Chapter 8:	Polynomials	8, 9, 31, 36		88–97
Chapter 9:	Factoring		13, 14	98–109
Chapter 10:	Solving Quadratic Equations	1, 44	1, 7, 8, 31	110–119
Chapter 11:	Graphing and Writing Equations and Inequalities	12, 14, 17, 20, 23, 34, 35, 41, 42, 43	9, 12, 16, 22, 25, 29, 39	120–145
Chapter 12:	Systems of Equations and Systems of Inequalities	24		146–153
Chapter 13:	Relations and Functions	40	5	154–162
Chapter 14:	Statistics		27, 28, 32, 42, 45	163–172
Chapter 15:	Probability	18	40, 44	173–179

Chapter 1
Numbers and Number Systems

1.1 Real Numbers

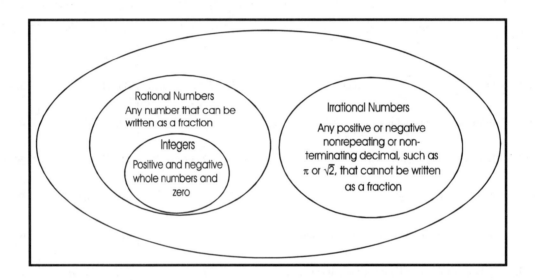

Real numbers include all positive and negative numbers and zero. Included in the set of real numbers are positive and negative fractions, decimals, and rational and irrational numbers.

Use the diagram above and your calculator to answer the following questions.

1. Using your calculator, find the square root of 7. Does it repeat? Does it end? Is it a rational or an irrational number?

2. Find $\sqrt{25}$. Is it rational or irrational? is it an integer?

3. Is an integer an irrational number?

4. Is an integer a real number?

5. Is $\frac{1}{8}$ a real number? Is it rational or irrational?

Identity the following numbers as rational (R) or (I).

6. 5π

7. $\sqrt{8}$

8. $\frac{1}{3}$

9. -7.2

10. $-\frac{3}{4}$

11. $\frac{\sqrt{2}}{2}$

12. $9 + \pi$

13. 1.0004

14. $-\frac{4}{5}$

15. $1.1\overline{8}$

16. $\sqrt{81}$

17. $\frac{\pi}{4}$

18. $-\sqrt{36}$

19. $17\frac{1}{2}$

20. $-\frac{5}{3}$

1.2   Integers

In elementary school, you learned to use whole numbers.

Whole numbers $= \{0, 1, 2, 3, 4, 5, ...\}$

For most things in life, whole numbers are all we need to use. However, when a checking account falls below zero or the temperature falls below zero, we need a way to express that. Mathematicians have decided that a negative sign, which looks exactly like a subtraction sign, would be used in front of a number to show that the number is below zero. All the negative whole numbers and positive whole numbers plus zero make up the set of integers.

Integers $= \{..., -4, -3, -2, -1, 0, 1, 2, 3, 4, ...\}$

1.3   Absolute Value

The absolute value of a number is the distance the number is from zero on the number line.

The absolute value if 6 is written $|6|$. $|6| = 6$
The absolute value of -6 is written $|-6|$. $|-6| = 6$

Both 6 and -6 are the same distance, 6 spaces, from zero so their absolute value is the same: 6.

Examples:

$|-4| = 4$ $-|-4| = -4$ $|-9| + 5 = 9 + 5 = 14$
$|9| - |8| = 9 - 8 = 1$ $|6| - |-6| = 6 - 6 = 0$ $|-5| + |-2| = 5 + 2 = 7$

Simplify the following absolute value problems.

1. $|9| = $ _____

2. $-|5| = $ _____

3. $|-25| = $ _____

4. $-|-12| = $ _____

5. $-|64| = $ _____

6. $|-2| = $ _____

7. $-|-3| = $ _____

8. $|-4| - |3| = $ _____

9. $|-8| - |-4| = $ _____

10. $|5| + |-4| = $ _____

11. $|-2| + |6| = $ _____

12. $|10| + |8| = $ _____

13. $|-2| + |4| = $ _____

14. $|-3| + |-4| = $ _____

15. $|7| - |-5| = $ _____

1.4   Multiplying and Dividing Absolute Values

When multiplying and dividing absolute values, one must apply the rules of absolute values before multiplying or dividing.

Example 1:   Multiply: $|6| \times |-8|$

Step 1:   Apply the absolute value rule, which states that the absolute value of any number, positive or negative, is that number as a positive.
$$|6| = 6 \quad \text{and} \quad |-8| = 8$$

Step 2:   Multiply. $6 \times 8 = \mathbf{48}$

Example 2:   Divide: $|-6| \div -|3|$

Step 1:   Apply the absolute value rules.
$$|-6| = 6 \quad \text{and} \quad -|3| = -3$$

Step 2:   Divide. $6 \div -3 = \mathbf{-2}$

Solve the problems below using the rules for absolute values.

1. $|-4| \div |2 - 5| \quad =$

2. $|12| \div -|-3| \quad =$

3. $\dfrac{|-14|}{|-2|} \quad =$

4. $-|15| \div |3| \quad =$

5. $|-3| \times -|-7| \quad =$

6. $|-1 \times 5| \quad =$

7. $|-1| \times -|-4| \quad =$

8. $|3|\,(|2|) \quad =$

9. $|2|\,(-|5|) \quad =$

10. $3 \times |-7| \quad =$

11. $|-12| \cdot -|2| \quad =$

12. $\dfrac{-|-18|}{|-6|} \quad =$

13. $-21 \div |-7| \quad =$

14. $-|5| \times |3| \quad =$

15. $|-6|\,(|7|) \quad =$

16. $\dfrac{|-3|}{|-3|} \quad =$

17. $|-5| \times |-8| \quad =$

18. $\dfrac{-|12|}{|-6|} \quad =$

19. $8\,(-|4|) \quad =$

20. $|-1| \cdot |-8| \quad =$

21. $|-7| \cdot |-4| \quad =$

22. $|-2| \div -|2| \quad =$

23. $\dfrac{|18|}{|-6|} \quad =$

24. $|5|\,(-|3|) \quad =$

1.5   Order of Operations

In long math problems with $+$, $-$, $\times$, $\div$, $()$, and exponents in them, you have to know what to do first. Without following the same rules, you could get different answers. If you will memorize the silly sentence, Please Excuse My Dear Aunt Sally, you can memorize the order you must follow.

Please   "P" stands for parentheses. You must get rid of parentheses first.
Examples: $3(1+4) = 3(5) = 15$
$6(10-6) = 6(4) = 24$

Excuse   "E" stands for exponents. You must eliminate exponents next.
Example: $4^2 = 4 \times 4 = 16$

My Dear   "M" stands for multiply. "D" stands for divide. Start on the left of the equation and perform all multiplications and divisions in the order in which they appear.

Aunt Sally   "A" stands for add. "S" stands for subtract. Start on the left and perform all additions and subtractions in the order they appear.

Example 3: $12 \div 2(6-3) + 3^2 - 1$		
Please	Eliminate **parentheses**. $6-3 = 3$ so now we have	$12 \div 2(3) + 3^2 - 1$
Excuse	Eliminate **exponents**. $3^2 = 9$ so now we have	$12 \div 2(3) + 9 - 1$
My Dear	**Multiply** and **divide** next in order from left to right.	$12 \div 2 = 6$ then $6(3) = 18$
Aunt Sally	Last, we **add** and **subtract** in order from left to right.	$18 + 9 - 1 = 26$

Simplify the following problems.

1. $6 + 9 \times 2 - 4$

2. $3(4+2) - 6^2$

3. $3(6-3) - 2^3$

4. $49 \div 7 - 3 \times 3$

5. $10 \times 4 - (7-2)$

6. $2 \times 3 \div 6 \times 4$

7. $4^3 \div 8(4+2)$

8. $7 + 8(14-6) \div 4$

9. $(2+8-12) \times 4$

10. $4(8-13) \times 4$

11. $8 + 4^2 \times 2 - 6$

12. $3^2(4+6) + 3$

13. $(12-6) + 27 \div 3^2$

14. $82^0 - 1 + 4 \div 2^2$

15. $1 - (2-3) + 8$

16. $12 - 4(7-2)$

17. $18 \div (6+3) - 12$

18. $10^2 + 3^3 - 2 \times 3$

19. $4^2 + (7+2) \div 3$

20. $7 \times 4 - 9 \div 3$

When a problem has a fraction bar, simplify the top of the fraction (numerator) and the bottom of the fraction (denominator) separately using the rules for order of operations. You treat the top and bottom as if they were separate problems. Then reduce the fraction to lowest terms.

Example 4: $\dfrac{2\,(4-5)-6}{5^2+3\,(2+1)}$

| Please | Eliminate **parentheses**. $(4-5)=-1$ and $(2+1)=3$ | $\dfrac{2\,(-1)-6}{5^2+3\,(3)}$ |

| Excuse | Eliminate **exponents**. $5^2=25$ | $\dfrac{2\,(-1)-6}{25+3\,(3)}$ |

| My Dear | **Multiply** and **divide** in the numerator and denominator separately. $3\,(3)=9$ and $2\,(-1)=-2$ | $\dfrac{-2-6}{25+9}$ |

| Aunt Sally | **Add** and **subtract** in the numerator and denominator separately. $-2-6=-8$ and $25+9=34$ | $\dfrac{-8}{34}$ |

Now reduce the fraction to lowest terms. $\dfrac{-8}{34}=\dfrac{-4}{17}$

Simplify the following problems.

1. $\dfrac{2^2+4}{5+3\,(8+1)}$

6. $\dfrac{(9-3)+3^2}{-5-2\,(4+1)}$

11. $\dfrac{-3\,(9-7)}{7+9-2^3}$

2. $\dfrac{8^2-(4+11)}{4^2-3^2}$

7. $\dfrac{16-3\,(10-6)}{(13+15)-5^2}$

12. $\dfrac{4-(2+7)}{13+(6-9)}$

3. $\dfrac{5-2\,(4-3)}{2\,(1-8)}$

8. $\dfrac{(2-5)-11}{12-2\,(3+1)}$

13. $\dfrac{5\,(3-8)-2^2}{7-3\,(6+1)}$

4. $\dfrac{10+(2-4)}{4\,(2+6)-2^2}$

9. $\dfrac{7+(8-16)}{6^2-5^2}$

14. $\dfrac{3\,(3-8)+5}{8^2-(5+9)}$

5. $\dfrac{3^3-8\,(1+2)}{-10-(3+8)}$

10. $\dfrac{16-(12-3)}{8\,(2+3)-5}$

15. $\dfrac{6^2-4\,(7+3)}{8+(9-3)}$

1.6   Estimated Solutions

In the real world, estimates can be very useful. The best approach to finding estimates is to round off all numbers in the problem. Then solve the problem, and choose the closest answer. If money problems have both dollars and cents, round to the nearest dollar or ten dollars. $44.86 rounds to $40.

Example 5:   Which is a reasonable answer? $1580 \div 21$

A. 80   B. 800   C. 880   D. 8000

Step 1:   Round off the numbers in the problem. 1580 rounds to 1600   21 rounds to 20

Step 2:   Work the problem. $1600 \div 20 = 80$ The closest answer is A. 80.

Choose the best answer below.

1. Which is a reasonable answer? 544×12
   (A) 54
   (B) 500
   (C) 540
   (D) 5400

2. Jeff buys a pair of pants for $45.95, a belt for $12.97, and a dress shirt for $24.87. Estimate about how much he spends.
   (A) $60
   (B) $70
   (C) $80
   (D) $100

3. For lunch, Marcia eats a sandwich with 187 calories, a glass of skim milk with 121 calories, and 2 brownies with 102 calories each. About how many calories does she consume?
   (A) 300
   (B) 350
   (C) 480
   (D) 510

4. Which is a reasonable answer? $89,900 \div 28$
   (A) 300
   (B) 500
   (C) 1000
   (D) 3000

5. Which is a reasonable answer? $74,295 - 62,304$

   (A) $12,000$

   (B) $11,000$

   (C) $10,000$

   (D) 1000

6. Delia buys 4 cans of soup at $0.99 each, a box of cereal for $4.78, and 2 frozen dinners at $3.89 each. About how much does she spend?

   (A) $10.00

   (B) $11.00

   (C) $13.00

   (D) $17.00

7. Which is the best estimate? $22,480 + 5516$

   (A) 2800

   (B) $17,000$

   (C) $28,000$

   (D) $32,000$

8. Which is the best estimate? $23,895 \div 599$

   (A) $20.00

   (B) $30.00

   (C) $40.00

   (D) $50.00

9. Tracy needs a pack of paper, 2 folders, a protractor, and 6 pencils. Using the chart below, about how much money does she need?

   (A) $3.00

   (B) $4.00

   (C) $5.00

   (D) $6.00

10. Jake needs 2 pencils, 3 erasers, a binder, and a compass. About how much money will he need according to the chart below?

   (A) $6.00

   (B) $7.00

   (C) $8.00

   (D) $9.00

School Store Price List

Pencils	Erasers	Folders	Binders	Compass	Protractor	Paper	Pens
2 for $0.78	$0.59	$0.21	$2.79	$1.59	$0.89	$1.29	$1.10

1.7   Understanding Exponents

Sometimes it is necessary to multiply a number by itself one or more times. For example, a math problem may need to multiply 3×3 or $5 \times 5 \times 5 \times 5$. In these situations, mathematicians have come up with a shorter way of writing out this kind of multiplication. Instead of writing 3×3, you can write 3^2, or instead of writing $5 \times 5 \times 5 \times 5$, 5^4 means the same thing. The first number is the **base**. The small, raised number is called the **exponent** or **power**. The exponent tells how many times the base should be multiplied by itself.

Example 6: 6^3 ← **exponent (or power)**, ← **base**   This means multiply by 6 three times: $6 \times 6 \times 6$

Example 7:   **Negative numbers can be raised to exponents also.**
An **even** exponent will give a **positive** answer: $(-2)^2 = (-2) \times (-2) = 4$
An **odd** exponent will give a **negative** answer: $(-2)^3 = (-2) \times (-2) \times (-2) = (-8)$

You also need to know two special properties of exponents:

> 1. **Any base number raised to the exponent of 1 equals the base number**
> 2. **Any base number raised to the exponent of 0 equals 1.**

Example 8: $4^1 = 4$ $10^1 = 10$ $25^1 = 25$ $4^0 = 1$ $10^0 = 1$ $25^0 = 1$

Rewrite the following problems using exponents.

Example 9: $2 \times 2 \times 2 = 2^3$

1. $7 \times 7 \times 7 \times 7$
2. 10×10
3. $12 \times 12 \times 12$
4. $4 \times 4 \times 4 \times 4$

5. $9 \times 9 \times 9$
6. 25×25
7. $15 \times 15 \times 15$
8. $5 \times 5 \times 5 \times 5 \times 5$

9. $2 \times 2 \times 2 \times 2$
10. 14×14
11. $3 \times 3 \times 3 \times 3 \times 3$
12. $11 \times 11 \times 11$

Use your calculator to figure what product each number with an exponent represents.

Example 10: $2^3 = 2 \times 2 \times 2 = 8$

13. $(-8)^3$
14. 12^2
15. 20^1

16. 5^4
17. 15^0
18. 16^2

19. $(-10)^2$
20. 3^5
21. 10^4

22. 7^0
23. 4^3
24. 54^1

Express each of the following numbers as a base with an exponent.

Example 11: $4 = 2 \times 2 = 2^2$

25. 9
26. 16
27. 27

28. 36
29. 8
30. 32

31. 1000
32. 125
33. 81

34. 64
35. 49
36. 121

1.8   Multiplication with Exponents

Rule 1:   To multiply two expressions with the same base, add the exponents together and keep the base the same.

Example 12: $2^3 \times 2^5 = 2^{3+5} = 2^8$

Rule 2:   If a power is raised to another power, multiply the exponents together and keep the base the same.

Example 13: $(2^3)^2 = 2^{3\times2} = 2^6$

Rule 3:   If a product in parenthesis is raised to a power, then each factor is raised to the power when parenthesis are eliminated.

Example 14: $(2 \times 4)^2 = 2^2 \times 4^2 = 4 \times 16 = 64$

Example 15: $(3a)^3 = 3^3 \times a^3 = 27a^3$

Example 16: $(7b^5)^2 = 7^2 b^{10} = 49b^{10}$

Simplify each of the expressions below.

1. $(5^3)^2$

2. $6^3 \times 6^5$

3. $4^3 \times 4^3$

4. $(7^5)^2$

5. $(6^2)^5$

6. $2^5 \times 2^3$

7. $(4 \times 5)^2$

8. $(3^4)^0$

9. $(3^3)^2$

10. $2^5 \times 2^5$

11. $(3 \times 3)^2$

12. $(2a)^4$

13. $(3^2)^4$

14. $4^5 \times 4^3$

15. $(3 \times 2)^4$

16. $(5^2)^2$

17. $(6 \times 4)^2$

18. $(9a^5)^3$

19. $4^3 \times 4^4$

20. $(6b^5)^2$

21. $(5^2)^3$

22. $3^7 \times 3^3$

23. $(3a)^2$

24. $(3^4)^2$

25. $(4^4)^2$

26. $(2b^3)^4$

27. $(5a^2)^5$

28. $(8a^3)^2$

29. $(9^2)^2$

30. $10^5 \times 10^4$

31. $(3 \times 5)^2$

32. $(7^3)^2$

1.9   Division with Exponents

Rule 1:   Expressions can also have negative exponents. Negative exponents do not indicate negative numbers. They indicate reciprocals, which is 1 over the original number.

Example 17: $2^{-3} = \dfrac{1}{2^3} = \dfrac{1}{8}$

Example 18: $3a^{-5} = 3 \times \dfrac{1}{a^5} = \dfrac{3}{a^5}$

Rule 2:   When dividing expressions with exponents that have the same base, subtract the exponents. Expressions in simplified form only have positive exponents.

Example 19: $\dfrac{3^5}{3^3} = 3^{5-3} = 3^2 = 9$

Example 20: $\dfrac{3^5}{3^8} = 3^{5-8} = 3^{-3} = \dfrac{1}{3^3} = \dfrac{1}{27}$

Rule 3:   If a fraction is raised to a power, then both the numerator and the denominator are raised to the same power.

Example 21: $\left(\dfrac{3}{4}\right)^3 = \dfrac{3^3}{4^3} = \dfrac{27}{64}$

Example 22: $(2x)^{-2} = \dfrac{1}{(2x)^2} = \dfrac{1}{4x^2}$

Reduce the following expressions to their simplest form. All exponents should be positive.

1. $5x^{-4}$

2. $\dfrac{2^2}{2^4}$

3. $\left(\dfrac{2}{3}\right)^2$

4. $6a^{-2}$

5. $\dfrac{3^6}{3^3}$

6. $(5a)^{-2}$

7. $\dfrac{3^4}{3^3}$

8. $\left(\dfrac{7}{8}\right)^3$

9. $(6a)^{-2}$

10. $\dfrac{(x^2)^3}{x^4}$

11. $\dfrac{(3y)^3}{3^2 y}$

12. $\dfrac{(3a^2)^3}{a^4}$

13. $(2x^2)^{-5}$

14. $2x^{-2}$

15. $(a^3)^{-2}$

16. $(2^{-2})^3$

17. $\left(\dfrac{1}{2}\right)^2$

18. $\dfrac{1}{3^{-2}}$

19. $(4y)^{-5}$

20. $4y^{-5}$

1.10   Square Root

Just as working with exponents is related to multiplication, so finding square roots is related to division. In fact, the sign for finding the square root of a number looks similar to a division sign. The best way to learn about square roots is to look at examples.

Example 23:   This is a square root problem: $\sqrt{64}$
It is asking, "What is the square root of 64?"
It means, "What number multiplied by itself equals 64?"
The answer is 8. $8 \times 8 = 64$.

Find the square root of the following numbers.

$\sqrt{36}$ $6 \times 6 = 36$ so $\sqrt{36} = 6$ $\sqrt{144}$ $12 \times 12 = 144$ so $\sqrt{144} = 12$

Find the square roots of the following numbers.

1. $\sqrt{49}$ 6. $\sqrt{625}$ 11. $\sqrt{4}$

2. $\sqrt{81}$ 7. $\sqrt{100}$ 12. $\sqrt{900}$

3. $\sqrt{25}$ 8. $\sqrt{289}$ 13. $\sqrt{64}$

4. $\sqrt{16}$ 9. $\sqrt{196}$ 14. $\sqrt{9}$

5. $\sqrt{121}$ 10. $\sqrt{36}$ 15. $\sqrt{144}$

1.11   Adding and Subtracting Roots

You can add and subtract terms with square roots only if the number under the square root sign is the same.

Example 24: $2\sqrt{2} + 3\sqrt{2} = 5\sqrt{2}$

Example 25: $12\sqrt{7} - 3\sqrt{7} - 9\sqrt{7}$

Or, look at the following examples where you can simplify the square roots and then add or subtract.

Example 26: $2\sqrt{25} + \sqrt{36}$

    Step 1:   Simplify. You know that $\sqrt{25} = 5$, and $\sqrt{36} = 6$ so the problem simplifies to $2(5) + 6$

Step 2:   Solve: $2(5) + 6 = 10 + 6 = 16$

Example 27: $2\sqrt{72} - 3\sqrt{2}$

Step 1:   Simplify what you know. $\sqrt{72} = \sqrt{36 \cdot 2} = 6\sqrt{2}$

Step 2:   Substitute $6\sqrt{2}$ for $\sqrt{72}$ simplify.
$2(6)\sqrt{2} - 3\sqrt{2} = 12\sqrt{2} - 3\sqrt{2} = 9\sqrt{2}$

Simplify the following addition and subtraction problems.

1. $3\sqrt{5} + 9\sqrt{5}$

2. $3\sqrt{25} + 4\sqrt{16}$

3. $4\sqrt{8} + 2\sqrt{2}$

4. $3\sqrt{32} - 2\sqrt{2}$

5. $\sqrt{25} - \sqrt{49}$

6. $2\sqrt{5} + 4\sqrt{20}$

7. $5\sqrt{8} - 3\sqrt{72}$

8. $\sqrt{27} + 3\sqrt{27}$

9. $3\sqrt{20} - 4\sqrt{45}$

10. $4\sqrt{45} - \sqrt{75}$

11. $2\sqrt{28} + 2\sqrt{7}$

12. $\sqrt{64} + \sqrt{81}$

13. $5\sqrt{54} - 2\sqrt{24}$

14. $\sqrt{32} + 2\sqrt{50}$

15. $2\sqrt{7} + 4\sqrt{63}$

16. $8\sqrt{2} + \sqrt{8}$

17. $2\sqrt{8} - 4\sqrt{32}$

18. $\sqrt{36} + \sqrt{100}$

19. $\sqrt{9} + \sqrt{25}$

20. $\sqrt{64} - \sqrt{36}$

21. $\sqrt{75} + \sqrt{108}$

22. $\sqrt{81} + \sqrt{100}$

23. $\sqrt{192} - \sqrt{75}$

24. $3\sqrt{5} + \sqrt{245}$

1.12   Multiplying Roots

You can also multiply square roots. To multiply square roots, you just multiply the numbers under the square root sign and then simplify. Look at the examples below.

Example 28: $\sqrt{2} \times \sqrt{6}$

Step 1: $\sqrt{2} \times \sqrt{6} = \sqrt{2 \times 6} = \sqrt{12}$ Multiply the numbers under the square root sign.

Step 2: $\sqrt{12} = \sqrt{4 \times 3} = 2\sqrt{3}$ Simplify.

Example 29: $3\sqrt{3} \times 5\sqrt{6}$

Step 1: $(3 \times 5)\sqrt{3 \times 6} = 15\sqrt{18}$ Multiply the numbers in front of the square root, and multiply the numbers under the square root sign.

Step 2: $15\sqrt{18} = 15\sqrt{2 \times 9}$
$15 \times 3\sqrt{2} = 45\sqrt{2}$ Simplify.

Example 30: $\sqrt{14} \times \sqrt{42}$ For this more complicated multiplication problem, use the rule of roots that you learned on page 12, $\sqrt{a \cdot b} = \sqrt{a} \cdot \sqrt{b}$.

Step 1: $\sqrt{14} = \sqrt{7} \times \sqrt{2}$ and
$\sqrt{42} = \sqrt{2} \times \sqrt{3} \times \sqrt{7}$ Instead of multiplying 14 by 42, divide these numbers into their roots.

$\sqrt{14} \times \sqrt{42} = \sqrt{7} \times \sqrt{2} \times \sqrt{2} \times \sqrt{3} \times \sqrt{7}$

Step 2:   Since you know that $\sqrt{7} \times \sqrt{7} = 7$ and $\sqrt{2} \times \sqrt{2} = 2$, the problem simplifies to
$(7 \times 2)\sqrt{3} = 14\sqrt{3}$

Simplify the following multiplication problems.

1. $\sqrt{5} \times \sqrt{7}$

2. $\sqrt{32} \times \sqrt{2}$

3. $\sqrt{10} \times \sqrt{14}$

4. $2\sqrt{3} \times 3\sqrt{6}$

5. $4\sqrt{2} \times 2\sqrt{10}$

6. $\sqrt{5} \times 3\sqrt{15}$

7. $\sqrt{45} \times \sqrt{27}$

8. $5\sqrt{21} \times \sqrt{7}$

9. $\sqrt{42} \times \sqrt{21}$

10. $4\sqrt{3} \times 2\sqrt{12}$

11. $\sqrt{56} \times \sqrt{24}$

12. $\sqrt{11} \times 2\sqrt{33}$

13. $\sqrt{13} \times \sqrt{26}$

14. $2\sqrt{2} \times 5\sqrt{5}$

15. $\sqrt{6} \times \sqrt{12}$

1.13   Dividing Roots

When dividing a number or a square root by another square root, you cannot leave the square root sign in the denominator (the bottom number) of a fraction. You must simplify the problem so that the square root is not in the denominator. Look at the examples below.

Example 31: $\dfrac{\sqrt{2}}{\sqrt{5}}$

Step 1: $\dfrac{\sqrt{2}}{\sqrt{5}} \times \dfrac{\sqrt{5}}{\sqrt{5}} \longleftarrow$ The fraction $\frac{\sqrt{5}}{\sqrt{5}}$ is equal to 1, and multiplying by 1 does not change the value of a number.

Step 2: $\dfrac{\sqrt{2 \times 5}}{5} = \dfrac{\sqrt{10}}{5}$ Multiply and simplify. Since $\sqrt{5} \times \sqrt{5}$ equals 5, you no longer have a square root in the denominator.

Example 32: $\dfrac{6\sqrt{2}}{2\sqrt{10}}$ In this problem, the numbers outside of the square root will also simplify.

Step 1: $\dfrac{6}{2} = 3$ so you have $\dfrac{3\sqrt{2}}{\sqrt{10}}$

Step 2: $\dfrac{3\sqrt{2}}{\sqrt{10}} \times \dfrac{\sqrt{10}}{\sqrt{10}} = \dfrac{3\sqrt{2 \times 10}}{10} = \dfrac{3\sqrt{20}}{10}$

Step 3: $\dfrac{3\sqrt{20}}{10}$ will further simplify because $\sqrt{20} = 2\sqrt{5}$, so you then have $\dfrac{3 \times 2\sqrt{5}}{10}$ which reduces to $\dfrac{3\sqrt{5}}{5}$.

Simplify the following division problems.

1. $\dfrac{9\sqrt{3}}{\sqrt{5}}$

2. $\dfrac{16}{\sqrt{8}}$

3. $\dfrac{24\sqrt{10}}{12\sqrt{3}}$

4. $\dfrac{\sqrt{121}}{\sqrt{6}}$

5. $\dfrac{\sqrt{40}}{\sqrt{90}}$

6. $\dfrac{33\sqrt{15}}{11\sqrt{2}}$

7. $\dfrac{\sqrt{32}}{\sqrt{12}}$

8. $\dfrac{\sqrt{11}}{\sqrt{5}}$

9. $\dfrac{\sqrt{2}}{\sqrt{6}}$

10. $\dfrac{2\sqrt{7}}{\sqrt{14}}$

11. $\dfrac{5\sqrt{2}}{4\sqrt{8}}$

12. $\dfrac{4\sqrt{21}}{7\sqrt{7}}$

13. $\dfrac{9\sqrt{22}}{2\sqrt{2}}$

14. $\dfrac{\sqrt{35}}{2\sqrt{14}}$

15. $\dfrac{\sqrt{40}}{\sqrt{15}}$

16. $\dfrac{\sqrt{3}}{\sqrt{12}}$

1.14   Estimating Square Roots

Example 33:   Estimate the value of $\sqrt{3}$.

Step 1:   Estimate the value of $\sqrt{3}$ by using the square root of values that you know. $\sqrt{1}$ is 1 and $\sqrt{4}$ is 2, so the value of $\sqrt{3}$ is going to be between 1 and 2.

Step 2:   To estimate a little closer, try squaring 1.5. $1.5 \times 1.5 = 2.25$, so $\sqrt{3}$ has to be greater than 1.5. If you do further trial-and-error calculations, you will find that $\sqrt{3}$ is greater than 1.7 ($1.7 \times 1.7 = 2.89$) but less than 1.8 ($1.8 \times 1.8 = 3.24$).

Therefore $\sqrt{3}$ is around 1.75. It is closer to 2 than it is to 1.

Example 34: Is the $\sqrt{52}$ closer to 7 or 8? Look at the perfect square above and below 52.

To answer this question, first look at 7^2 which is equal to 49 and 8^2 which is equal to 64. Then ask yourself whether 52 is closer to 49 or 64. The answer is 49, of course. Therefore, the $\sqrt{52}$ is closer to 7 than 8.

Follow the steps above to answer the following questions. Do not use a calculator.

1. Is $\sqrt{66}$ closer to 8 or 9?

2. Is $\sqrt{27}$ closer to 5 or 6?

3. Is $\sqrt{13}$ closer to 3 or 4?

4. Is $\sqrt{78}$ closer to 8 or 9?

5. Is $\sqrt{12}$ closer to 3 or 4?

6. Is $\sqrt{8}$ closer to 2 or 3?

7. Is $\sqrt{20}$ closer to 4 or 5?

8. Is $\sqrt{53}$ closer to 7 or 8?

9. Is $\sqrt{60}$ closer to 7 or 8?

10. Is $\sqrt{6}$ closer to 2 or 3?

1.15   Properties of Addition and Multiplication

The Associative, Commutative, and Distributive properties and the Identity of Addition and Multiplication are listed below by example as a quick refresher.

Property	Example
1. Associative Property of Addition	$(a+b)+c = a+(b+c)$
2. Associative Property of Multiplication	$(a \times b) \times c = a \times (b \times c)$
3. Commutative Property of Addition	$a+b = b+a$
4. Commutative Property of Multiplication	$a \times b = b \times a$
5. Distributive Property	$a \times (b+c) = (a \times b) + (a \times c)$
6. Identity Property of Addition	$0+a = a$
7. Identity Property of Multiplication	$1 \times a = a$
8. Inverse Property of Addition	$a+(-a) = 0$
9. Inverse Property of Multiplication	$a \times \dfrac{1}{a} = \dfrac{a}{a} = 1, a \neq 0$

Write the number of the property listed above that describes each of the following statements.

1. $4+5 = 5+4$

2. $4+(2+8) = (4+2)+8$

3. $10(4+7) = (10)(4)+(10)(7)$

4. $(2 \times 3) \times 4 = 2 \times (3 \times 4)$

5. $1 \times 12 = 12$

6. $8\left(\dfrac{1}{8}\right) = 1$

7. $1c = c$

8. $18+0 = 18$

9. $9+(-9) = 0$

10. $p \times q = q \times p$

11. $t+0 = t$

12. $x(y+z) = xy + xz$

13. $(m)(n \cdot p) = (m \cdot n)(p)$

14. $-y+y = 0$

Chapter 1 Review

Simplify the following problems.

1. 15^0

2. $\sqrt{100}$

3. $\sqrt{49}$

4. $(-3)^3$

5. $5^2 \times 5^3$

6. $(4^4)^3$

7. $(3a^2)^{-2}$

8. $6x^{-3}$

9. $\dfrac{4^6}{4^4}$

10. $\left(\dfrac{3}{5}\right)^2$

11. $\dfrac{(3a^2)^3}{a^3}$

12. $\dfrac{6x^{-2}}{x^{-3}}$

Write as exponents.

13. $3 \times 3 \times 3 \times 3$

14. $6 \times 6 \times 6 \times 6 \times 6 \times 6$

15. $11 \times 11 \times 11$

16. $2 \times 2 \times 2 \times 2 \times 2 \times 2 \times 2 \times 2$

Solve the following absolute value problems.

17. $|4|$

18. $|-6|$

19. $|-3| + |7|$

20. $|8| - |-5|$

Simplify the following problems using the correct order of operations.

21. $10 \div (-1 - 4) + 2$

22. $\dfrac{10 + 5^2 - 3}{2^2 + 2(5 - 3)}$

23. $5 - 5^2 + (2 - 4)$

24. $(8 - 10) \times (5 + 3) - 10$

25. $5 + (2)(4 - 1) \div 3$

26. $1 - (9 - 1) \div 2$

27. $\dfrac{5(3 - 6) + 3^2}{4(2 + 1) - 6}$

28. $-4(6 + 4) \div (-2) + 1$

29. $12 \div (7 - 4) - 2$

30. $1 + 4^2 \div (3 + 1)$

Estimate the following square root solutions.

31. Is $\sqrt{5}$ closer to 2 or 3?

32. Is $\sqrt{52}$ closer to 7 or 8?

33. Is $\sqrt{130}$ closer to 11 or 12?

34. Is $\sqrt{619}$ closer to 24 or 25?

Chapter 2
Fractions, Decimals, and Percents

2.1 Adding Fractions

Example 1:   Add $3\frac{1}{2} + 2\frac{2}{3}$

Step 1:   Rewrite the problem vertically, and find a common denominator.
Think: What is the smallest number I can divide 2 and 3 into without a remainder? 6, of course.

$$
\begin{array}{rcl}
3\frac{1}{2} & = & \frac{}{6} \\[2mm]
+2\frac{2}{3} & = & \frac{}{6} \\
\hline
\end{array}
$$

Step 2:   To find the numerator for the top fraction, think: What do I multiply 2 by to get 6? You must multiply the top and bottom numbers of the fraction by 3 to keep the fraction equal. For the bottom fraction, multiply the top and bottom number by 2.

Step 3:   Add whole numbers and fractions, and simplify.

$$
\begin{array}{rclcl}
3\frac{1}{2} & = & 3\frac{3}{6} & & \\[2mm]
+2\frac{2}{3} & = & 2\frac{4}{6} & & \\
\hline
& = & 5\frac{7}{6} & = & 6\frac{1}{6}
\end{array}
$$

Add and simplify the answers.

1. $3\frac{5}{9}$ $+5\frac{2}{3}$

3. $3\frac{3}{4}$ $+2\frac{3}{5}$

5. $6\frac{5}{6}$ $+4\frac{1}{3}$

7. $\frac{1}{3}$ $+7\frac{3}{4}$

9. $4\frac{7}{10}$ $+8\frac{2}{3}$

11. $3\frac{3}{11}$ $+2\frac{3}{4}$

2. $1\frac{1}{4}$ $+4\frac{2}{5}$

4. $2\frac{1}{4}$ $+1\frac{7}{8}$

6. $9\frac{1}{5}$ $+5\frac{5}{6}$

8. $9\frac{4}{9}$ $+3\frac{2}{3}$

10. $5\frac{2}{7}$ $+\frac{1}{2}$

12. $\frac{3}{5}$ $+\frac{4}{9}$

2.2 Multiplying Fractions

Example 2: Multiply $4\frac{3}{8} \times \frac{8}{10}$

Step 1: Change the mixed numbers in the problem to improper fractions. To change $4\frac{3}{8}$ to a mixed number, multiply the denominator by the whole number, add the numerator to this result, and put this total over the old denominator. The denominator is 8, the whole number is 4, and the numerator is 3. To change $4\frac{3}{8}$ to a mixed number, multiply 8×4, add 3, and put this total over 8. The mixed number is then $\frac{35}{8}$. The problem is now to multiply $\frac{35}{8} \times \frac{8}{10}$.

Step 2: When multiplying fractions, you can cancel and simplify terms that have a common factor. The 8 in the first fraction will cancel with the 8 in the second fraction.

$$\frac{35}{\cancel{8}} \times \frac{\cancel{8}}{10}$$

The terms 35 and 10 are both divisible by 5, so

35 simplifies to 7, and 10 simplifies to 2. $\quad \overset{7}{\frac{\cancel{35}}{1}} \times \frac{1}{\underset{2}{\cancel{10}}}$

Step 3: Multiply the simplified fractions. $\qquad \frac{7}{1} \times \frac{1}{2} = \frac{7}{2}$

Step 4: You cannot leave an improper fraction as the answer, so to change $\frac{7}{2}$ back to a mixed number, divide 7 by 2, and put the remainder over the denominator as a fraction. The whole number will be $7 \div 2$, or 3, and since the remainder is 1, the fraction will be $\frac{1}{2}$. The improper fraction $\frac{7}{2}$ is equal to $3\frac{1}{2}$.

Multiply and reduce your answers to lowest terms.

1. $3\frac{1}{5} \times 1\frac{1}{2}$

5. $1\frac{1}{2} \times 1\frac{2}{5}$

9. $6\frac{2}{5} \times 5$

13. $2\frac{1}{2} \times 5\frac{4}{5}$

2. $\frac{3}{8} \times 3\frac{3}{7}$

6. $3\frac{3}{7} \times \frac{5}{6}$

10. $6 \times 1\frac{3}{8}$

14. $7\frac{2}{3} \times \frac{3}{4}$

3. $4\frac{1}{3} \times 2\frac{1}{4}$

7. $3 \times 6\frac{1}{3}$

11. $\frac{5}{7} \times 2\frac{1}{3}$

15. $2 \times 3\frac{1}{4}$

4. $4\frac{2}{3} \times 3\frac{3}{4}$

8. $1\frac{1}{6} \times 8$

12. $1\frac{2}{5} \times 1\frac{1}{4}$

16. $3\frac{1}{8} \times 1\frac{3}{5}$

2.3   Dividing Fractions

Example 3: $1\dfrac{3}{4} \div 2\dfrac{5}{8}$

Step 1:   Change the mixed numbers in the problem to improper fractions.

$$1\frac{3}{4} = \frac{(4 \times 1) + 3}{4} = \frac{7}{4} \text{ and } 2\frac{5}{8} = \frac{(8 \times 2) + 5}{8} = \frac{21}{8}.$$

The problem is now $\dfrac{7}{4} \div \dfrac{21}{8}$.

Step 2:   Invert (turn upside down) the second fraction and multiply. $\dfrac{7}{4} \times \dfrac{8}{21}$

Step 3:   Cancel where possible and multiply. $\dfrac{1}{1}\dfrac{\cancel{7}}{\cancel{4}} \times \dfrac{\cancel{8}}{\cancel{21}}\dfrac{2}{3} = \dfrac{2}{3}$

Divide and reduce answers to lowest terms.

1. $2\dfrac{2}{3} \div 1\dfrac{7}{9}$

2. $5 \div 1\dfrac{1}{2}$

3. $1\dfrac{5}{8} \div 2\dfrac{1}{4}$

4. $8\dfrac{2}{3} \div 2\dfrac{1}{6}$

5. $2\dfrac{4}{5} \div 2\dfrac{1}{5}$

6. $3\dfrac{2}{3} \div 1\dfrac{1}{6}$

7. $10 \div \dfrac{4}{5}$

8. $6\dfrac{1}{4} \div 1\dfrac{1}{2}$

9. $\dfrac{2}{5} \div 2$

10. $4\dfrac{1}{6} \div 1\dfrac{2}{3}$

11. $9 \div 3\dfrac{1}{4}$

12. $5\dfrac{1}{3} \div 2\dfrac{2}{5}$

13. $4\dfrac{1}{5} \div \dfrac{9}{10}$

14. $2\dfrac{2}{3} \div 4\dfrac{4}{5}$

15. $3\dfrac{3}{8} \div 3\dfrac{6}{7}$

16. $5\dfrac{1}{4} \div \dfrac{3}{4}$

2.4   Comparing the Relative Magnitude of Fractions

Comparing the relative magnitude of fractions using the greater than (>), less than (<), and equal to (=) signs.

Example 4:   Compare $\dfrac{3}{4}$ and $\dfrac{5}{8}$

Step 1:   Find the lowest common denominator. The lowest common denominator is 8.

Step 2:   Change fourths to eighths by multiplying three fourths by two halves,

$$\frac{2}{2} \times \frac{3}{4} = \frac{6}{8}.$$

Step 3: $\dfrac{6}{8} > \dfrac{5}{8}$

Therefore, $\dfrac{3}{4} > \dfrac{5}{8}$.

Example 5: Compare the mixed numbers $1\frac{3}{5}$ and $1\frac{2}{3}$.

Step 1: Change the mixed numbers to improper fractions (explained in the previous lesson).

$1\frac{3}{5} = \frac{8}{5}$ and $1\frac{2}{3} = \frac{5}{3}$

Step 2: Find the lowest common denominator for the improper fractions. The lowest common denominator is 15.

Step 3: Change fifths to fifteenths and thirds to fifteenths, $\frac{3 \times 8}{3 \times 5} = \frac{24}{15}$ and $\frac{5 \times 5}{5 \times 3} = \frac{25}{15}$.

Step 4: $\frac{24}{15} < \frac{25}{15}$ therefore $1\frac{3}{5} < 1\frac{2}{3}$.

Fill in the box with the correct sign ($>$, $<$, or $=$).

1. $\frac{7}{9} \square \frac{7}{8}$

2. $\frac{6}{7} \square \frac{5}{6}$

3. $\frac{4}{6} \square \frac{5}{7}$

4. $\frac{3}{10} \square \frac{4}{13}$

5. $\frac{5}{8} \square \frac{4}{11}$

6. $\frac{5}{8} \square \frac{4}{7}$

7. $\frac{9}{10} \square \frac{8}{13}$

8. $\frac{2}{13} \square \frac{1}{10}$

9. $\frac{4}{9} \square \frac{3}{5}$

10. $\frac{2}{6} \square \frac{4}{5}$

11. $\frac{7}{12} \square \frac{6}{11}$

12. $\frac{3}{11} \square \frac{5}{12}$

2.5 Changing Fractions to Decimals

Example 6: Change $\frac{1}{8}$ to a decimal.

Step 1: To change a fraction to a decimal, simply divide the top number by the bottom number. $8 \overline{\smash{)}1}$

Step 2: Add a decimal point and a 0 after the 1 and divide.

$$
\begin{array}{r}
0.1 \\
8 \overline{\smash{)}1.0} \\
-8 \\
\hline
2
\end{array}
$$

Step 3: Continue adding 0's and dividing until there is no remainder.

$$
\begin{array}{r}
0.125 \\
8 \overline{\smash{)}1.0} \\
-8 \\
\hline
20 \\
-16 \\
\hline
40 \\
-40 \\
\hline
0
\end{array}
$$

In some problems, the number after the decimal point begins to repeat. Take, for example, the fraction $\frac{4}{11}$. $4 \div 11 = 0.363636$, and the 36 keeps repeating forever. To show that the 36 repeats, simply write a bar above the numbers that repeat, $0.\overline{36}$.

Change the following fractions to decimals.

1. $\dfrac{4}{5}$ 5. $\dfrac{1}{10}$ 9. $\dfrac{3}{5}$ 13. $\dfrac{7}{9}$ 17. $\dfrac{3}{16}$

2. $\dfrac{2}{3}$ 6. $\dfrac{5}{8}$ 10. $\dfrac{7}{10}$ 14. $\dfrac{9}{10}$ 18. $\dfrac{3}{4}$

3. $\dfrac{1}{2}$ 7. $\dfrac{5}{6}$ 11. $\dfrac{4}{11}$ 15. $\dfrac{1}{4}$ 19. $\dfrac{8}{9}$

4. $\dfrac{5}{9}$ 8. $\dfrac{1}{6}$ 12. $\dfrac{1}{9}$ 16. $\dfrac{3}{8}$ 20. $\dfrac{5}{12}$

2.6   Changing Percents to Decimals and Decimals to Percents

To change a **percent** to a **decimal**, move the **decimal** point two places to the left, and drop the **percent** sign. If there is no decimal point shown, it is understood to be after the number and before the percent sign. Sometimes you will need to add a "0". (See 5% below.)

Example 7: $14\% = 0.14$ $5\% = 0.05$ $100\% = 1$ $103\% = 1.03$

$\nearrow$

(decimal point)

Change the following percents to decimal numbers.

1. $18\% = $_____   8. $119\% = $_____   15. $5\% = $_____

2. $23\% = $_____   9. $7\% = $_____   16. $25\% = $_____

3. $9\% = $_____   10. $55\% = $_____   17. $410\% = $_____

4. $63\% = $_____   11. $80\% = $_____   18. $1\% = $_____

5. $4\% = $_____   12. $17\% = $_____   19. $50\% = $_____

6. $45\% = $_____   13. $66\% = $_____   20. $99\% = $_____

7. $2\% = $_____   14. $13\% = $_____   21. $107\% = $_____

To change a decimal to a percent, move the decimal two places to the right, and add a percent sign. You may need to add a "0". (See 0.8 below.)

Example 8: $0.62 = 62\%$ $0.07 = 7\%$ $0.8 = 80\%$
$0.166 = 16.6\%$ $1.54 = 154\%$

Change the following decimal numbers to percents.

22. 0.15

23. 0.62

24. 1.53

25. 0.22

26. 0.35

27. 0.375

28. 0.648

29. 0.044

30. 0.58

31. 0.86

32. 0.29

33. 0.06

34. 0.48

35. 3.089

36. 0.042

37. 0.375

38. 5.09

39. 0.75

40. 0.3

41. 2.9

42. 0.06

2.7   Changing Percents to Fractions and Fractions to Percents

Example 9:   Change 15% to a fraction.

Step 1:   Copy the number without the percent sign. 15 is the top number of the fraction.

Step 2:   The bottom number of the fraction is 100.

$$15\% = \frac{15}{100}$$

Step 3:   Reduce the fraction. $\frac{15}{100} = \frac{3}{20}$

Change the following percents to fractions and reduce.

1. 50%

2. 13%

3. 22%

4. 95%

5. 52%

6. 63%

7. 75%

8. 91%

9. 18%

10. 3%

11. 25%

12. 5%

13. 16%

14. 1%

15. 79%

16. 40%

17. 99%

18. 30%

19. 15%

20. 84%

Example 10:   Change $\dfrac{7}{8}$ to a percent.

Step 1:   Divide 7 by 8. Add as many 0's as necessary.

$$
\begin{array}{r}
.875 \\
8\,\overline{)\,7.000} \\
-\ \ 64 \\
\hline
60 \\
-\ \ 56 \\
\hline
40 \\
-\ \ 40 \\
\hline
0
\end{array}
$$

Step 2:   Change the decimal answer, 0.875, to a percent by moving the decimal point 2 places to the right.

$$\frac{7}{8} = .875 = 87.5\%$$

Change the following fractions to percents.

1. $\dfrac{1}{5}$

2. $\dfrac{5}{8}$

3. $\dfrac{7}{16}$

4. $\dfrac{3}{8}$

5. $\dfrac{3}{16}$

6. $\dfrac{19}{100}$

7. $\dfrac{1}{10}$

8. $\dfrac{4}{5}$

9. $\dfrac{15}{16}$

10. $\dfrac{3}{4}$

11. $\dfrac{1}{8}$

12. $\dfrac{5}{16}$

13. $\dfrac{1}{16}$

14. $\dfrac{1}{4}$

15. $\dfrac{4}{100}$

16. $\dfrac{3}{4}$

17. $\dfrac{2}{5}$

18. $\dfrac{16}{25}$

2.8   Comparing the Relative Magnitude of Numbers

When comparing the relative magnitude of numbers, the greater than (>), less than (<), and the equal to (=) signs are the ones most frequently used. The simplest way to compare numbers that are in different notations, like percent, decimals, and fractions, is to change all of them to one notation. Decimals are the easiest to compare.

Example 11:   Which is larger: $1\dfrac{1}{4}$ or 1.3?

Step 1:   Change $1\dfrac{1}{4}$ to a decimal. $\dfrac{1}{4} = .25$, so $1\dfrac{1}{4} = 1.25$.

Step 2:   Compare the two values in decimal form.
$1.25 < 1.3$, so 1.3 is the larger of the two values.

Example 12: Which is smaller: 60% or $\frac{2}{3}$?

Step 1: Change both values to decimals.
$60\% = 0.6$ and $\frac{2}{3} = 0.\overline{66}$

Step 2: Compare the two values in decimal form.
0.6 is smaller than $0.\overline{66}$, so $60\% < \frac{2}{3}$.

Fill in each box with the correct sign.

1. $23.4 \ \square \ 23\frac{1}{2}$

2. $17\% \ \square \ .17$

3. $\frac{3}{8} \ \square \ 37.5\%$

4. $25\% \ \square \ \frac{2}{10}$

5. $234\% \ \square \ 23.4$

6. $\frac{1}{7} \ \square \ 14\%$

7. $13.95 \ \square \ 13\frac{8}{9}$

8. $4.0 \ \square \ 40\%$

9. $25\% \ \square \ \frac{3}{2}$

10. $\frac{12}{4} \ \square \ 300\%$

11. $6\% \ \square \ \frac{1}{16}$

12. $1.\overline{33} \ \square \ \frac{4}{3}$

13. $.8 \ \square \ \frac{4}{5}$

14. $75\% \ \square \ \frac{3}{4}$

15. $\frac{5}{8} \ \square \ 62\%$

Compare the sums, differences, products, and quotients below. Fill in each box with the correct sign.

16. $(32 + 15) \ \square \ (65 - 17)$

17. $(45 - 13) \ \square \ (31 + 9)$

18. $(24 \div 4) \ \square \ (24 \div 6)$

19. $(48 \div 6) \ \square \ (4 \times 3)$

20. $(4 \times 3) \ \square \ (48 \div 6)$

21. $(18 \times 4) \ \square \ (5 \times 17)$

22. $[(1 + 3) + 5] \ \square \ [5 + (3 + 1)]$

23. $[1 + (3 + 5)] \ \square \ [(5 - 3) + 1]$

24. $(25 \div 5) \ \square \ (5 \times 5)$

25. $(6 + 4 \div 2) \ \square \ [(6 + 4) \div 2]$

Chapter 2 Review

Add, multiply, or divide the following fractions.

1. $1\frac{2}{3} + 3\frac{3}{4}$ 3. $6\frac{1}{2} \times 5\frac{1}{3}$ 5. $7\frac{3}{5} \div 3\frac{1}{2}$

2. $11\frac{3}{8} + 9\frac{1}{10}$ 4. $\frac{4}{5} \times 8\frac{1}{6}$ 6. $4\frac{4}{5} \div 2\frac{1}{7}$

Change to a fraction.

7. 0.55 8. 0.84 9. 0.32

Change to a decimal.

10. $5\frac{3}{25}$ 11. $\frac{7}{100}$ 12. $10\frac{2}{3}$

Change the following percents to decimals.

13. 45% 14. 219% 15. 22% 16. 1.25%

Change the following decimals to percents.

17. 0.52 18. 0.64 19. 1.09 20. 0.625

Change the following percents to fractions.

21. 25% 22. 3% 23. 68% 24. 102%

Change the following fractions to percents.

25. $\dfrac{9}{10}$ 26. $\dfrac{5}{16}$ 27. $\dfrac{1}{8}$ 28. $\dfrac{1}{4}$

Use the $>$, $<$, and $=$ signs to make the following correct.

29. $\frac{5}{6} \ \square \ \frac{4}{5}$ 30. $\frac{3}{7} \ \square \ \frac{4}{8}$ 31. $\frac{4}{15} \ \square \ \frac{5}{16}$ 32. $\frac{3}{4} \ \square \ \frac{13}{16}$

Fill in the box with the correct sign: $<$, $>$, or $=$.

33. $(54 \div 6) \ \square \ (8 \times 7)$ 34. $[3 + (5 - 2)] \ \square \ [1 + (6 - 2)]$

Chapter 3
Introduction to Graphing

3.1 Graphing on a Number Line

Number lines allow you to graph values of positive and negative numbers as well as zero. Any real number, whether it is a fraction, decimal, or integer can be plotted on a number line. Number lines can be horizontal or vertical. The examples below illustrate how to plot different types of numbers on a number line.

3.2 Graphing Fractional Values

Example 1: What number does point A represent on the number line below?

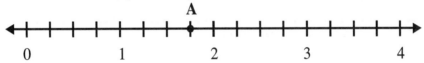

Step 1: Point A is between the numbers 1 and 2, so it is greater than 1 but less than 2. We can express the value of A as a fractional value that falls between 1 and 2. To do so, copy the integer that point A falls between which is closer to zero on the number line. In this case, copy the 1 because 1 is closer to zero on the number line than the 2.

Step 2: Count the number of spaces between each integer. In this case, there are 4 spaces between the 1 and the 2. Put this number as the bottom number in your fraction.

Step 3: Count the number of spaces between the 1 and the point A. Point A is 3 spaces away from number 1. Put this number as the top number in your fraction.

The integer that point A falls between that is closest to 0

Point A is at $1\frac{3}{4}$ ←← The number of spaces between 1 and A / The number of spaces between 1 and 2

Example 2: What number does point B represent on the number line below?

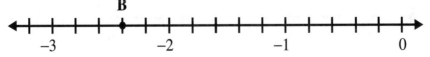

Step 1:   Point B is between -2 and -3. Again, we can express the value of B as a fraction that falls between -2 and -3. Copy the integer that point B falls between which is closer to zero. The -2 is closer to zero than -3, so copy -2.

Step 2:   In this example, there are 5 spaces between each integer. Five will be the bottom number in the fraction.

Step 3:   There are 2 spaces between -2 and point B. Two will be the top number in the fraction.

Point B is at $-2\frac{2}{5}$

Determine and record the value of each point on the number lines below.

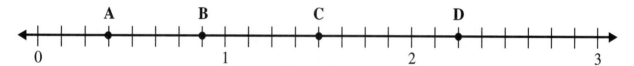

1.   A = _____   B = _____   C = _____   D = _____

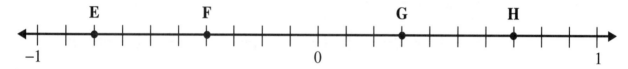

2.   E = _____   F = _____   G = _____   H = _____

3.   I = _____   J = _____   K = _____   L = _____

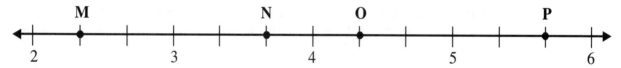

4.   M = _____   N = _____   O = _____   P = _____

5.   Q = _____   R = _____   S = _____   T = _____

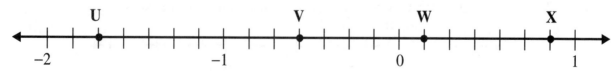

6.   U = _____   V = _____   W = _____   X = _____

3.3   Recognizing Improper Fractions, Decimals, and Square Root Values on a Number Line

Improper fractions, decimal values, and square root values can also be plotted on a number line. Study the examples below.

Example 3:   Where would $\frac{4}{3}$ fall on the number line below?

Step 1:   Convert the improper fraction to a mixed number. $\frac{4}{3} = 1\frac{1}{3}$

Step 2: $1\frac{1}{3}$ is $\frac{1}{3}$ of the distance between the numbers 1 and 2. Estimate this distance by dividing the distance between points 1 and 2 into thirds. Plot the point at the first division.

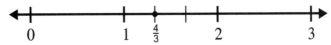

Example 4:   Plot the value of -1.75 on the number line below.

Step 1:   Convert the value -1.75 to a mixed fraction. $-1.75 = -1\frac{3}{4}$

Step 2: $-1\frac{3}{4}$ is $\frac{3}{4}$ of the distance between the numbers -1 and -2. Estimate this distance by dividing the distance between points -1 and -2 into fourths. Plot the point at the third division.

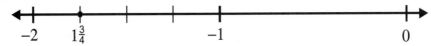

Example 5:   Plot the value of $\sqrt{3}$ on the number line below.

Step 1:   Estimate the value of $\sqrt{3}$ by using the square root of values that you know. $\sqrt{1} = 1$ and $\sqrt{4} = 2$, so the value of $\sqrt{3}$ is going to be between 1 and 2.

Step 2:   To estimate a little closer, try squaring 1.5. $1.5 \times 1.5 = 2.25$, so $\sqrt{3}$ has to be greater than 1.5. If you do further trial and error calculations, you will find that $\sqrt{3}$ is greater than 1.7 ($1.7 \times 1.7 = 2.89$) but less than 1.8 ($1.8 \times 1.8 = 3.24$).

Step 3:   Plot $\sqrt{3}$ around 1.75.

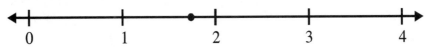

Plot and label the following values on the number lines given below.

1. $A = \dfrac{5}{4}$ $B = \dfrac{12}{5}$ $C = \dfrac{2}{3}$ $D = -\dfrac{3}{2}$

2. $E = 1.4$ $F = -2.25$ $G = -0.6$ $H = 0.625$

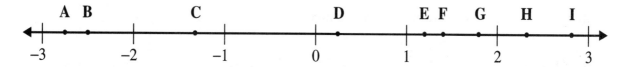

3. $I = \sqrt{2}$ $J = \sqrt{5}$ $K = \sqrt{6}$ $L = \sqrt{8}$

Match the correct value for each point on the on the number line below.

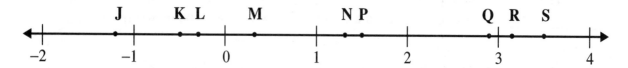

4. $1.8 = $ ____

5. $\dfrac{7}{3} = $ ____

6. $\sqrt{2} = $ ____

7. $-\dfrac{5}{2} = $ ____

8. $-2.75 = $ ____

9. $-\dfrac{4}{3} = $ ____

10. $\sqrt{8} = $ ____

11. $\dfrac{6}{5} = $ ____

12. $0.25 = $ ____

13. $\sqrt{12} = $ ____

14. $-0.5 = $ ____

15. $\dfrac{5}{4} = $ ____

16. $\dfrac{1}{3} = $ ____

17. $1.5 = $ ____

18. $-0.3 = $ ____

19. $-\dfrac{6}{5} = $ ____

20. $\sqrt{10} = $ ____

21. $2.9 = $ ____

3.4 Plotting Points on a Vertical Number Line

Number lines can also be drawn up and down (**vertical**) instead of across the page (**horizontal**). You plot points on a vertical number line the same way as you do on a horizontal number line.

Record the value represented by each point on the number lines below.

1. A = _____
2. B = _____
3. C = _____
4. D = _____
5. E = _____
6. F = _____
7. G = _____
8. H = _____

17. Q = _____
18. R = _____
19. S = _____
20. T = _____
21. U = _____
22. W = _____
23. X = _____
24. Y = _____

9. I = _____
10. J = _____
11. K = _____
12. L = _____
13. M = _____
14. N = _____
15. P = _____
16. Q = _____

25. A = _____
26. B = _____
27. C = _____
28. D = _____
29. E = _____
30. G = _____
31. H = _____
32. I = _____

3.5   Cartesian Coordinates

A number line allows you to graph points with only one value. A **Cartesian coordinate plane** allows you to graph points with two values. A Cartesian coordinate plane is made up of two number lines. The horizontal number line is called the **x-axis**, and the vertical number line is called the **y-axis**. The point where the x and y axes intersect is called the **origin**. The x and y axes separate the Cartesian coordinate plane into four quadrants that are labeled I, II, III, and IV. The quadrants are labeled and explained on the graph below. Each point graphed on the plane is designated by an **ordered pair** of coordinates. For example, $(2, -1)$ is an ordered pair of coordinates designated by **point B** on the plane below. The first number, 2, tells you to go over positive two on the x-axis. The -1 tells you to then go down negative one on the y-axis.

Remember: The first number always tells you how far to go right or left of 0, and the second number always tells you how far to go up or down from 0.

Quadrant II:
The x-coordinate is negative, and the y-coordinate is positive $(-,+)$.

Quadrant III:
Both coordinates in the ordered pair are negative $(-,-)$.

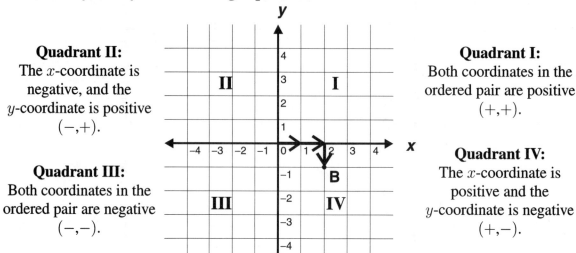

Quadrant I:
Both coordinates in the ordered pair are positive $(+,+)$.

Quadrant IV:
The x-coordinate is positive and the y-coordinate is negative $(+,-)$.

Plot and label the following points on the Cartesian coordinate plane provided.

A. $(2,4)$ K. $(-1,-1)$

B. $(-1,5)$ L. $(3,-3)$

C. $(3,-4)$ M. $(5,5)$

D. $(-5,-2)$ N. $(-2,-2)$

E. $(5,3)$ O. $(0,0)$

F. $(-7,-6)$ P. $(0,4)$

G. $(-2,5)$ Q. $(2,0)$

H. $(6,-1)$ R. $(-4,0)$

I. $(4,-7)$ S. $(0,-2)$

J. $(6,2)$ T. $(5,1)$

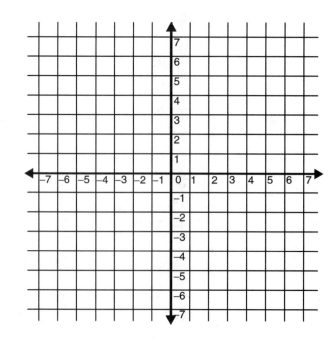

3.6 Identifying Ordered Pairs

When identifying ordered pairs, count how far left or right of 0 to find the x-coordinate and then how far up or down from 0 to find the y-coordinate.

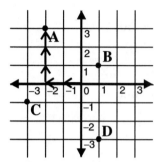

Point A: Left (negative) two and up (positive) three $= (-2,3)$ in quadrant II

Point B: Right (positive) one and up (positive) one $= (1,1)$ in quadrant I

Point C: Left (negative) three and down (negative) one $= (-3, -1)$ in quadrant III

Point D: Right (positive) one and down (negative) three $= (1, -3)$ in quadrant IV

Fill in the ordered pair for each point, and tell which quadrant it is in.

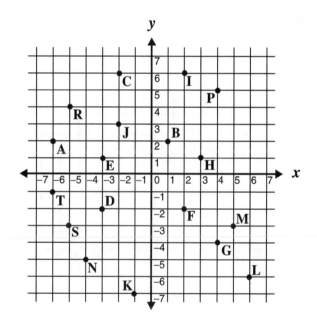

1. point A = (,   ) quadrant____

2. point B = (,   ) quadrant____

3. point C = (,   ) quadrant____

4. point D = (,   ) quadrant____

5. point E = (,   ) quadrant____

6. point F = (,   ) quadrant____

7. point G = (,   ) quadrant____

8. point H = (,   ) quadrant____

9. point I = (,   ) quadrant____

10. point J = (,   ) quadrant____

11. point K = (,   ) quadrant____

12. point L = (,   ) quadrant____

13. point M = (, ·) quadrant____

14. point N = (,   ) quadrant____

15. point P = (,   ) quadrant____

16. point R = (,   ) quadrant____

17. point S = (,   ) quadrant____

18. point T = (,   ) quadrant____

Sometimes, points on a coordinate plane fall on the x or y axis. If a point falls on the x-axis, then the second number of the ordered pair is 0. If a point falls on the y-axis, the first number of the ordered pair is 0.

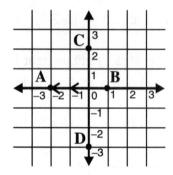

Point A: Left (negative) two and up zero $= (-2,0)$

Point B: Right (positive) one and up zero $= (1,0)$

Point C: Left/right zero and up (positive) two $= (0,2)$

Point D: Left/right zero and down (negative) three $= (0,-3)$

Fill in the ordered pair for each point.

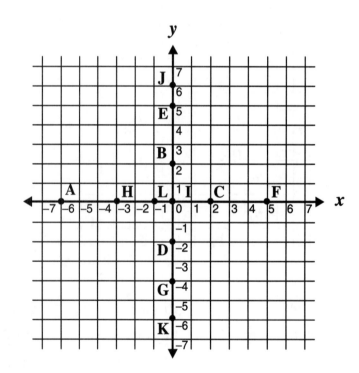

1. point A = (,   )

2. point B = (,   )

3. point C = (,   )

4. point D = (,   )

5. point E = (,   )

6. point F = (,   )

7. point G = (,   )

8. point H = (,   )

9. point I = (,   )

10. point J = (,   )

11. point K = (,   )

12. point L = (,   )

Chapter 3 Review

1.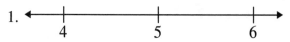

Plot and label $5\frac{3}{5}$ on the number line above.

2.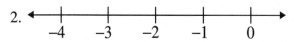

Plot and label $-3\frac{1}{2}$ on the number line above.

3.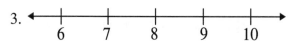

Plot and label 7.2 on the number line above.

4.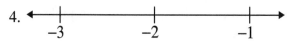

Plot and label -2.3 on the number line above.

Record the value represented by the point on the number line for questions 5–10.

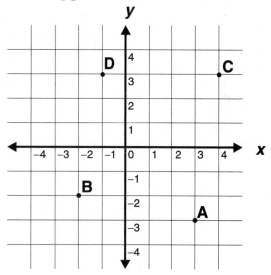

5. A _____

6. B _____

7. C _____

8. D _____

9. E _____

10. F _____

Record the coordinates and quadrants of the following points.

	Coordinates	Quadrants
11. A =	_____	_____
12. B =	_____	_____
13. C =	_____	_____
14. D =	_____	_____

On the same plane above, label these additional coordinates.

15. $E = (0, -3)$

16. $F = (-3, -1)$

17. $G = (4, 0)$

18. $H = (2, 2)$

Answer the following questions.

19. In which quadrant does the point $(2, 3)$ lie?

20. In which quadrant does the point $(-5, -2)$ lie?

Chapter 4
Introduction to Algebra

4.1   Algebra Vocabulary

Vocabulary Word	Example	Definition
variable	$4x$ (x is the variable)	a letter that can be replaced by a number
coefficient	$4x$ (4 is the coefficient)	a number multiplied by a variable or variables
term	$5x^2 + x - 2$ ($5x^2$, x, and -2 are terms)	numbers or variables separated by $+$ or $-$ signs
constant	$5x + 2y + 4$ (4 is a constant)	a term that does not have a variable
degree	$4x^2 + 3x - 2$ (the degree is 2)	the largest power of a variable in an expression
leading coefficient	$4x^2 + 3x - 2$ (4 is the leading coefficient)	the number multiplied by the term with the highest power
sentence	$2x = 7$ or $5 \leq x$	two algebraic expressions connected by $=, \neq, <, >, \leq, \geq$, or $\approx$
equation	$4x = 8$	a sentence with an equal sign
inequality	$7x < 30$ or $x \neq 6$	a sentence with one of the following signs: $\neq, <, >, \leq, \geq$, or $\approx$
base	6^3 (6 is the base)	the number used as a factor
exponent	6^3 (3 is the exponent)	the number of times the base is multiplied by itself

4.2   Substituting Numbers for Variables

These problems may look difficult at first glance, but they are very easy. Simply replace the variable with the number the variable is equal to, and solve the problems.

Example 1:   In the following problems, substitute 10 for a.

Problem	Calculation	Solution
1. $a + 1$	Simply replace the a with 10. $10 + 1$	11
2. $17 - a$	$17 - 10$	7
3. $9a$	This means multiply. 9×10	90
4. $\dfrac{30}{a}$	This means divide. $30 \div 10$	3
5. a^3	$10 \times 10 \times 10$	1000
6. $5a + 6$	$(5 \times 10) + 6$	56

Note: Be sure to do all multiplying and dividing before adding and subtracting.

Example 2:   In the following problems, let $x = 2$, $y = 4$, and $z = 5$.

Problem	Calculation	Solution
1. $5xy + z$	$5 \times 2 \times 4 + 5$	45
2. $xz^2 + 5$	$2 \times 5^2 + 5 = 2 \times 25 + 5$	55
3. $\dfrac{yz}{x}$	$(4 \times 5) \div 2 = 20 \div 2$	10

In the following problems, $t = 7$. Solve the problems.

1. $t + 3 =$

2. $18 - t =$

3. $\dfrac{21}{t} =$

4. $3t - 5 =$

5. $t^2 + 1 =$

6. $2t - 4 =$

7. $9t \div 3 =$

8. $\dfrac{t^2}{7} =$

9. $5t + 6 =$

10. $\dfrac{(t^2 - 7)}{6} =$

11. $4t + 5t =$

12. $\dfrac{6t}{3} =$

In the following problems $a = 4$, $b = -2$, $c = 5$, and $d = 10$. Solve the problems.

13. $4a + 2c =$

14. $3bc - d =$

15. $\dfrac{ac}{d} =$

16. $d - 2a =$

17. $a^2 - b =$

18. $abd =$

19. $5c - ad =$

20. $cd + bc =$

21. $\dfrac{6b}{a} =$

22. $9a + b =$

23. $5 + 3bc =$

24. $d^2 + d + 1 =$

4.3   Understanding Algebra Word Problems

The biggest challenge to solving word problems is figuring out whether to add, subtract, multiply, or divide. Below is a list of key words and their meanings. This list does not include every situation you might see, but it includes the most common examples.

Words Indicating Addition	**Example**	**Add**
and	6 **and** 8	$6 + 8$
increased	The original price of $15 **increased** by $5.	$15 + 5$
more	3 coins and 8 **more**	$3 + 8$
more than	Josh has 10 points. Will has 5 **more than** Josh.	$10 + 5$
plus	8 baseballs **plus** 4 baseballs	$8 + 4$
sum	the **sum** of 3 and 5	$3 + 5$
total	the **total** of 10, 14, and 15	$10 + 14 + 15$

Words Indicating Subtraction	**Example**	**Subtract**
decreased	$16 **decreased** by $5	$16 - 5$
difference	the **difference** between 18 and 6	$18 - 6$
less	14 days **less** 5	$14 - 5$
less than	Jose completed 2 laps **less than** Mike's 9.	*$9 - 2$
left	Ray sold 15 out of 35 tickets. How many did he have **left**?	*$35 - 15$
lower than	This month's rainfall is 2 inches **lower than** last month's rainfall of 8 inches.	*$8 - 2$
minus	15 **minus** 6	$15 - 6$

* In subtraction word problems, you cannot always subtract the numbers in the order that they appear in the problem. Sometimes the first number should be subtracted from the last. You must read each problem carefully.

Words Indicating Multiplication	**Example**	**Multiply**
double	Her $1000 profit doubled in in a month.	1000×2
half	Half of the $600 collected went to charity.	$\frac{1}{2} \times 600$
product	the product of 4 and 8	4×8
times	Li scored 3 times as many points as Ted who only scored 4.	3×4
triple	The bacteria tripled its original colony of 10, 000 in just one day.	$3 \times 10,000$
twice	Ron has 6 CD's. Tom has twice as many.	2×6

Words Indicating Division	**Example**	**Divide**
divide into, by, or among	The group of 70 divided into 10 teams	$70 \div 10$ or $\frac{70}{10}$
quotient	the quotient of 30 and 6	$30 \div 6$ or $\frac{30}{6}$

Match the phrase with the correct algebraic expression below. The answers will be used more than once.

A. $y - 2$

B. $2y$

C. $y + 2$

D. $\dfrac{y}{2}$

E. $2 - y$

1. 2 more than y

2. 2 divided into y

3. 2 less than y

4. twice y

5. the quotient of y and 2

6. y increased by 2

7. 2 less y

8. the product of 2 and y

9. y decreased by 2

10. y doubled

11. 2 minus y

12. the total of 2 and y

Now practice writing parts of algebraic expressions from the following word problems.

Example 3:   the product of 3 and a number, t Answer: $3t$

13. 3 less than x

14. y divided among 10

15. the sum of t and 5

16. n minus 14

17. 5 times k

18. the total of z and 12

19. double the number b

20. x increased by 1

21. the quotient t and 4

22. half of a number y

23. bacteria culture, b, doubled

24. triple John's age y

25. a number, n, plus 4

26. quantity, t, less 6

27. 18 divided by a number, x

28. n feet lower than 10

29. 3 more than p

30. the product of 4 and m

31. a number, y, decreased by 20

32. 5 times as much as x

4.4   Setting Up Algebra Word Problems

So far, you have seen only the first part of algebra word problems. To complete an algebra problem, an equal sign must be added. The words "**is**" or "**are**" as well as "**equal(s)**" signal that you should add an equal sign.

Example 4:   Double Jake's age, x, minus 4 is 22.

$$2x \ - \ 4 \ = \ 22$$

Translate the following word problems into algebra problems. DO NOT find the solutions to the problems yet.

1. Triple the original number, n, is $2,700$.

2. The product of a number, y, and 5 is equal to 15.

3. Four times the difference of a number, x, and 2 is 20.

4. The total, t, divided into 5 groups is 45.

5. The number of parts in inventory, p, minus 54 parts sold today is 320.

6. One-half an amount, x, added to $50 is $262

7. One hundred seeds divided by 5 rows equals n number of seeds per row.

8. A number, y, less than 50 is 82.

9. His base pay of $200 increased by his commission, x, is $500.

10. Seventeen more than half a number, h, is 35.

11. This month's sales of $2,300 are double January's sales, x.

12. The quotient of a number, w, and 4 is 32.

13. Six less a number, d, is 12.

14. Four times the sum of a number, y, and 10 is 48.

15. We started with x number of students. When 5 moved away, we had 42 left.

16. A number, b, divided into 36 is 12.

4.5   Changing Algebra Word Problems to Algebraic Equations

Example 5:   There are 3 people who have a total weight of 595 pounds. Sally weighs 20 pounds less than Jessie. Rafael weighs 15 pounds more than Jessie. How much does Jessie weigh?

Step 1:   Notice everyone's weight is given in terms of Jessie. Sally weighs 20 pounds less than Jessie Rafael weighs 15 pounds more than Jessie. First, we write everyone's weight in terms of Jessie, j.

$$
\begin{aligned}
\text{Jessie} &= j \\
\text{Sally} &= j - 20 \\
\text{Rafael} &= j + 15
\end{aligned}
$$

Step 2:   We know that all three together weigh 595 pounds. We write the sum of everyone's weight equal to 595.

$$j + j - 20 + j + 15 = 595$$

We will learn to solve these problems in the next chapter.

Change the following word problems to algebraic equations.

1. Fluffy, Spot, and Shampy have a combined age in dog years of 91. Spot is 14 years younger than Fluffy. Shampy is 6 years older than Fluffy. What is Fluffy's age, f, in dog years?

2. Jerry Marcosi puts 5% of the amount he makes per week into a retirement account, r. He is paid $11.00 per hour and works 40 hours per week for a certain number of weeks, w. Write an equation to help him find out how much he puts into his retirement account.

3. A furniture store advertises a 40% off liquidation sale on all items. What would the sale price (p) be on a $2530 dining room set?

4. Kyle Thornton buys an item which normally sells for a certain price, x. Today the item is selling for 25% off the regular price. A sales tax of 6% is added to the equation to find the final price, f.

5. Tamika Francois runs a floral shop. On Tuesday, Tamika sold total of $600 worth of flowers. The flowers cost her $100, and she paid an employee to work 8 hours for a given wage, w. Write an equation to help Tamika find her profit, p, on Tuesday.

6. Sharice is a waitress at a local restaurant. She makes an hourly wage of $3.50 plus she receives tips. On Monday, she works 6 hours and receives tip money, t. Write an equation showing what Sharice makes on Monday, y.

7. Jenelle buys x shares of stock in a company at $34.50 per share. She later sells the shares at $40.50 per share. Write an equation to show how much money, m, Jenelle has made.

Chapter 4 Review

Solve the following problems using $x = 2$.

1. $3x + 4 =$

2. $\dfrac{6x}{4} =$

3. $x^2 - 5 =$

4. $\dfrac{x^3 + 8}{2} =$

5. $12 - 3x =$

6. $x - 5 =$

7. $-5x + 4 =$

8. $9 - x =$

9. $2x + 2 =$

Solve the following problems. Let $w = -1$, $y = 3$, $z = 5$.

10. $5w - y =$

11. $wyz + 2 =$

12. $z - 2w =$

13. $\dfrac{3z + 5}{wz} =$

14. $\dfrac{6w}{y} + \dfrac{z}{w} =$

15. $25 - 2yz =$

16. $-2y + 3$

17. $4w - (yw) =$

18. $7y - 5z =$

For the following questions, write an equation to match each problem.

19. Calista earns $450 per week for a 40-hour work week plus $16.83 per hour for each hour of overtime after 40 hours. Write an equation that would be used to determine her weekly wages where w is her wages and v is the number of overtime hours worked.

20. Daniel purchased a 1-year CD, c, from a bank. He bought it at an annual interest rate of 6%. After 1 year, Daniel cashes in the CD. What is the total amount it is worth?

21. Omar is a salesman. He earns an hourly wage of $8.00 per hour plus he receives a commission of 7% on the sales he makes. Write an equation which would be used to determine his weekly salary, w, where x is the number of hours worked, and y is the amount of sales for the week.

22. Tom earns $500 per week before taxes are taken out. His employer takes out a total of 33% for state, federal, and Social Security taxes. Which expression below will help Tom figure his net pay?
    (A) $500 - .33$
    (B) $500 \div .33$
    (C) $500 + .33\,(500)$
    (D) $500 - .33\,(500)$

23. Rosa has to pay $100 of her medical expenses in a year before she qualifies for her insurance company to begin paying. After paying the $100 "deductible," her insurance company will pay 80% of her medical expenses. This year, her total medical expenses came to $960.00. Which expression below shows how much her insurance company will pay?

(A) $0.80\,(960 - 100)$

(B) $100 + (960 \div 0.80)$

(C) $960\,(100 - 0.80)$

(D) $0.80\,(960 + 100)$

24. A plumber charges $45 per hour plus a $25.00 service charge. If a represents his total charges in dollars and b represents the number of hours worked, which formula below could the plumber use to calculate his total charges?

(A) $a = 45 + 25b$

(B) $a = 45 + 25 + b$

(C) $a = 45b + 25$

(D) $a = (45)\,(25) + b$

(E) $a = 70b$

25. In 2004, Bell Computers informed its sales force to expect a 2.6% price increase on all computer equipment in the year 2005. A certain sales representative wanted to see how much the increase would be on a computer, c, that sold for $2200 in 2004. Which expression below will help him find the cost of the computer in the year 2005?

(A) $0.26\,(2200)$

(B) $2200 - 0.026\,(2200)$

(C) $2200 + 0.026\,(2200)$

(D) $0.026\,(2200) - 2200$

26. Juan sells a boat that he bought 5 years ago. He sells it for 60% less than he originally paid for it. If the original cost is b, write an expression that shows how much he sells the boat for.

27. Toshi is going to get a 7% raise after he works at his job for 1 year. If s represents his starting salary, write an expression that shows how much he will make after his raise.

Chapter 5
Ratios and Proportions

5.1   Ratio Problems

In some word problems, you may be asked to express answers as a **ratio**. Ratios can look like fractions. Numbers must be written in the order they are requested. In the following problem, 8 cups of sugar is mentioned before 6 cups of strawberries. But in the question part of the problem, you are asked for the ratio of STRAWBERRIES to SUGAR. The amount of strawberries IS THE FIRST WORD MENTIONED, so it must be the **top** number of the fraction. The amount of sugar, THE SECOND WORD MENTIONED, must be the **bottom** number of the fraction.

Example 1:   The recipe for jam requires 8 cups of sugar for every 6 cups of strawberries. What is the ratio of strawberries to sugar in this recipe?

$$\begin{array}{ll} \text{First number requested} & \dfrac{6}{8} \quad \dfrac{\text{cups strawberries}}{\text{cups sugar}} \\ \text{Second number requested} & \end{array}$$

Answers may be reduced to lowest terms. $\dfrac{6}{8} = \dfrac{3}{4}$

Practice writing ratios for the following word problems and reduce to lowest terms. DO NOT CHANGE ANSWERS TO MIXED NUMBERS. Ratios should be left in fraction form.

1. Out of the 248 seniors, 112 are boys. What is the ratio of boys to the total number of seniors?

2. It takes 7 cups of flour to make 2 loaves of bread. What is the ratio of cups of flour to loaves of bread?

3. A skyscraper that stands 620 feet tall casts a shadow that is 125 feet long. What is the ratio of the shadow to the height of the skyscraper?

4. Twenty boxes of paper weigh 520 pounds. What is the ratio of boxes to pounds?

5. The newborn weighs 8 pounds and is 22 inches long. What is the ratio of weight to length?

6. Jack pays $6.00 for 10 pounds of apples. What is the ratio of the price of apples to the pounds of apples?

7. Jordan spends $45 on groceries. Of that total, $23 is for steaks. What is the ratio of steak cost to the total grocery cost?

8. Madison's flower garden measures 8 feet long by 6 feet wide. What is the ratio of length to width?

5.2   Solving Proportions

Two **ratios (fractions)** that are **equal** to each other are called **proportions. For example,** $\frac{1}{4} = \frac{2}{8}$. **Read the following example to see how to find a number missing from a proportion.**

Example 2: $\dfrac{5}{15} = \dfrac{8}{x}$

Step 1:   To find x, you first multiply the two numbers that are diagonal to each other.

$$\dfrac{5}{\{15\}} = \dfrac{\{8\}}{x}$$

$15 \times 8 = 120$

$5 \times x = 5x$

Therefore, $5x = 120$

Step 2:   Then divide the product (120) by the other number in the proportion (5).

$120 \div 5 = 24$

Therefore, $\dfrac{5}{15} = \dfrac{8}{24}$ **and** $x = 24$.

Practice finding the number missing from the following proportions. First, multiply the two numbers that are diagonal from each other. Then divide by the other number.

1. $\dfrac{2}{5} = \dfrac{6}{x}$

2. $\dfrac{9}{3} = \dfrac{x}{5}$

3. $\dfrac{x}{12} = \dfrac{3}{4}$

4. $\dfrac{7}{x} = \dfrac{3}{9}$

5. $\dfrac{12}{x} = \dfrac{2}{5}$

6. $\dfrac{12}{x} = \dfrac{4}{3}$

7. $\dfrac{27}{3} = \dfrac{x}{2}$

8. $\dfrac{1}{x} = \dfrac{3}{12}$

9. $\dfrac{15}{2} = \dfrac{x}{4}$

10. $\dfrac{7}{14} = \dfrac{x}{6}$

11. $\dfrac{5}{6} = \dfrac{10}{x}$

12. $\dfrac{4}{x} = \dfrac{3}{6}$

13. $\dfrac{x}{5} = \dfrac{9}{15}$

14. $\dfrac{9}{18} = \dfrac{x}{2}$

15. $\dfrac{5}{7} = \dfrac{35}{x}$

16. $\dfrac{x}{2} = \dfrac{8}{4}$

17. $\dfrac{15}{20} = \dfrac{x}{8}$

18. $\dfrac{x}{40} = \dfrac{5}{100}$

5.3   Ratio and Proportion Word Problems

You can use ratios and proportions to solve problems.

Example 3:   A stick one meter long is held perpendicular to the ground and casts a shadow 0.4 meters long. At the same time, an electrical tower casts a shadow 112 meters long. Use ratio and proportion to find the height of the tower.

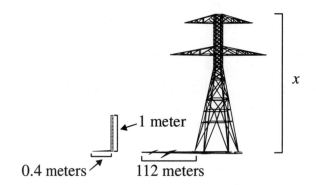

Step 1:   Set up a proportion using the numbers in the problem. Put the shadow lengths on one side of the equation and put the heights on the other side. The 1 meter height is paired with the 0.4 meter length, so let them both be top numbers. Let the unknown height be x.

$$\frac{\overset{\text{shadow length}}{.4}}{112} = \frac{\overset{\text{object height}}{1}}{x}$$

Step 2:   Solve the proportion as you did on page 1.

$$112 \times 1 = 112$$
$$112 \div .4 = 280$$

Answer: The tower height is 280 meters.

Use ratio and proportion to solve the following problems.

1. Rudolph can mow a lawn that measures 1000 square feet in 2 hours. At that rate, how long would it take him to mow a lawn 3500 square feet?

2. Faye wants to know how tall her school building is. On a sunny day, she measures the shadow of the building to be 6 feet. At the same time she measures the shadow cast by a 5 foot statue to be 2 feet. How tall is her school building?

3. Out of every 5 students surveyed, 2 listen to country music. At that rate, how many students in a school of 800 listen to country music?

4. Butterfly, a Labrador Retriever, has a litter of 8 puppies. Four are black. At that rate, how many puppies in a litter of 10 would be black?

5. According to the instructions on a bag of fertilizer, 5 pounds of fertilizer are needed for every 100 square feet of lawn. How many square feet will a 25-pound bag cover?

6. A race car can travel 2 laps in 5 minutes. At this rate, how long will it take the race car to complete 100 laps ?

7. If it takes 7 cups of flour to make 4 loaves of bread, how many loaves of bread can you make from 35 cups of flour?

8. If 3 pounds of jelly beans cost $6.30, how much would 2 pounds cost?

9. For the first 4 home football games, the concession stand sold a total of 600 hotdogs. If that ratio stays constant, how many hotdogs will sell for all 10 home games?

5.4   Direct and Indirect Variation

The graphs shown below represent functions where x varies with y directly or indirectly. Graph A shows direct variation. Graph B shows an indirect variation. In direct variation, when y increases, the x increases, and when y decreases, x decrease. In indirect variation, also called inverse variation, when y increases, x decreases, and when y decreases, x increases.

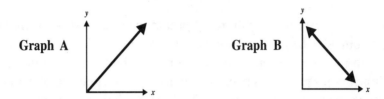

Example 4:   Direct and indirect variation can be determined by function tables.

Table 1	x	y
	0	3
	1	4
	2	7
	3	12
	4	19

Table 2	x	y
	0	20
	1	18
	2	16
	3	14
	4	12

Notice in Table 1, as x increases, y increases also. This means that function Table 1 represents a direct variation between x and y. On the other hand, Table 2 shows a decrease in y when x increases. This means that function Table 2 represents an indirect variation between x and y.

Direct variation occurs in a function when y varies directly, or in the same was, as x varies. The two values vary by a proportional factor, k. Direct variation is expressed in the equation $y = kx$.

Example 5:   If y varies directly with x and $y = 18$ when $x = 12$, what is the value of y when $x = 6$?

   Step 1:   Use the direct variation formula, $y = xk$, to solve for k:
   $$y = xk \quad \Rightarrow \quad 18 = 12(k) \quad \Rightarrow \quad \frac{18}{12} = \frac{12(k)}{12} \quad \Rightarrow \quad k = 1.5$$

   Step 2:   Use the given value of x, 6, and k, 1.5, to calculate the new value of y.
   $$y = xk \quad \Rightarrow \quad y = 6(1.5) \quad \Rightarrow \quad y = 9$$

For an **indirect variation**, y varies inversely with, or opposite of, x. With indirect variation, divide k, the proportional factor, by the value of x. Indirect variation is given by the equation $y = \dfrac{k}{x}$.

Example 6:   In a function, y varies inversely as x varies. If $y = 18$ when $x = 12$, what is the value of y when $x = 6$?

Step 1:   Use the formula to solve for k:

$$y = \frac{k}{x} \implies 18 = \frac{k}{12} \implies (18)(12) = \frac{k(12)}{12} \implies k = 216$$

Step 2:   Substitute 216 for k and the new value of x, 6, to find the new value of y.

$$y = \frac{k}{x} \implies y = \frac{216}{6} \implies y = 36$$

Direct and indirect variation can be used in word problems as well. For example, direct variation word problems work out just like proportion word problems. To review direct variation word problems, refer back to the last section. Indirect word problems, on the other hand, do not work exactly like proportional word problems because when one value goes up, the other one goes down. Working together problems represent one type of indirect variation problem.

Example 7:   It takes 45 minutes for 2 copiers to finish a printing job. If 5 copiers work together to print a job, how long would it take to finish?

Step 1:   It will take less time to finish a job if more computers work together. As the number of copiers increase, the number of minutes to complete the job decreases. Therefore, this is an indirect variation problem, and we will need to use the formula, $y = \frac{k}{x}$.

Step 2:   Find the value of x and y. Let y represent the number of minutes the copiers need to complete the job. Let x represent the number of copiers working to print the job. $y = 45$ minutes, and $x = 2$ computers.

Step 3:   Find k.

$$y = \frac{k}{x} \implies 45 = \frac{k}{2} \implies (45)(2) = \frac{k(2)}{2} \implies k = 90$$

Step 4:   Substitute 90 for k and the new value of x, 5 copier, to find the new value of y.

$$y = \frac{k}{x} \implies y = \frac{90}{5} \implies y = 18 \text{ minutes}$$

It will take 5 copiers only 18 minutes to complete the printing job.

Solve these direct variation problems.

1. If $y = 6$ and $x = 3$, what is the value of y when $x = 5$?
2. If $y = 10$ and $x = 5$, what is the value of y when $x = 4$?
3. If $y = 6$ and $x = 2$, what is the value of y when $x = 7$?
4. If $y = 8$ and $x = 4$, what is the value of y when $x = 6$?
5. If $y = 15$ and $x = 3$, what is the value of y when $x = 5$?

Solve these indirect variation problems.

6. If $y = 6$ and $x = 4$, what is the value of y when $x = 8$?
7. If $y = 12$ and $x = 6$, what is the value of y when $x = 8$?
8. If $y = 9$ and $x = 6$, what is the value of y when $x = 3$?
9. If $y = 6$ and $x = 5$, what is the value of y when $x = 3$?
10. If $y = 3$ and $x = 12$, what is the value of y when $x = 9$?

Chapter 5 Review

Solve the following proportions and ratios.

1. $\dfrac{8}{x} = \dfrac{1}{2}$

2. $\dfrac{2}{5} = \dfrac{x}{10}$

3. $\dfrac{x}{6} = \dfrac{3}{9}$

4. $\dfrac{4}{9} = \dfrac{8}{x}$

5. Out of the 100 coins, 45 are in mint condition. What is the ratio of mint condition coins to the total number of coins?

6. The ratio of boys to girls in the ninth grade is $6 : 5$. If there are 135 girls in the class, how many boys are there?

7. Twenty out of the total 235 seniors graduate with honors. What is the ratio of seniors graduating with honors to the total number of seniors?

8. Aunt Bess uses 3 cups of oatmeal to bake 6 dozen oatmeal cookies. How many cups of oatmeal would she need to bake 15 dozen cookies?

9. If $y = 12$ and $x = 6$, using indirect variation, what is the value of y when $x = 20$?

10. If $y = 10$ and $x = 5$, what is the value of y when $x = 4$? Use direct variation to solve.

11. If $y = 5$ and $x = 2$, what is the value of y when $x = 12$? Use indirect variation to solve.

Chapter 6
Solving One-Step Equations and Inequalities

6.1   One-Step Algebra Problems With Addition and Subtraction

You have been solving algebra problems since second grade by filling in blanks. For example, $5 + \underline{} = 8$. The answer is 3. You can solve the same kind of problems using algebra. The problems only look a little different because the blank has been replaced with a letter. The letter is called a **variable**.

Example 1:   **Arithmetic** $5 + \underline{} = 14$
                     Algebra $5 + x = 14$

The goal in any algebra problem is to move all the numbers to one side of the equal sign and have the letter (called a **variable**) on the other side. In this problem the 5 and the "x" are on the same side. The 5 is added to x. To move it, do the **opposite** of **add**. The **opposite** of **add** is **subtract**, so subtract 5 from both sides of the equation. Now the problem looks like this:

$$\begin{array}{r} 5 + x = 14 \\ -5 \qquad -5 \\ \hline x = 9 \end{array}$$ To check your answer, put 9 in place of x in the original problem. Does $5 + 9 = 14$? Yes, it does.

Example 2: $\begin{array}{r} y - 16 = 27 \\ +16 \quad +16 \\ \hline y = 43 \end{array}$ Again, the 16 has to move. To move it to the other side of the equation, we do the **opposite** of **subtract**. We **add** 16 to both sides. Check by putting 43 in place of the y in the original problem. Does $43 - 16 = 27$? Yes.

Solve the problems below.

1. $n + 9 = 27$ 6. $15 + x = 24$ 11. $k - 5 = 29$ 16. $t - 16 = 28$ 21. $r - 12 = 37$

2. $12 + y = 55$ 7. $w - 14 = 89$ 12. $a + 17 = 45$ 17. $m + 14 = 37$ 22. $h - 17 = 22$

3. $51 + v = 67$ 8. $t - 26 = 20$ 13. $d + 26 = 56$ 18. $y - 21 = 29$ 23. $x - 37 = 46$

4. $f + 16 = 31$ 9. $m - 12 = 17$ 14. $15 + x = 56$ 19. $f + 7 = 31$ 24. $r - 11 = 28$

5. $5 + x = 23$ 10. $c - 7 = 21$ 15. $y + 19 = 32$ 20. $h - 12 = 18$ 25. $t - 5 = 52$

6.2   One-Step Algebra Problems With Multiplication and Division

Solving one-step algebra problems with multiplication and division are just as easy as adding and subtracting. Again, you perform the **opposite** operation. If the problem is a **multiplication** problem, you **divide** to find the answer. If it is a **division** problem, you **multiply** to find the answer. Carefully read the examples below, and you will see how easy they are.

Example 3: $4x = 20$ (4x means 4 times x. 4 is the coefficient of x.)

The goal is to get the numbers on one side of the equal sign and the variable x on the other side. In this problem, the 4 and the x are on the same side of the equal sign. The 4 has to be moved over. $4x$ means 4 times x. The opposite of **multiply** is **divide**. If we divide both sides of the equation by 4, we will find the answer.

$4x = 20$ **We need to divide both sides by 4.**

This means divide by 4. $\longrightarrow$ $\dfrac{\overset{1}{\cancel{4}}x}{\underset{1}{\cancel{4}}} = \dfrac{\overset{5}{\cancel{20}}}{\underset{1}{\cancel{4}}}$ **We see that** $1x = 5$**, so** $x = 5$**.**

When you put 5 **in place of** x **in the original problem, it is correct.** $4 \times 5 = 20$

Example 4: $\dfrac{y}{4} = 2$

This problem means y divided by 4 is equal to 2. In this case, the opposite of divide is multiply. We need to multiply both sides of the equation by 4.

$\cancel{4} \times \dfrac{y}{\cancel{4}} = 2 \times 4$ so $y = 8$

When you put 8 **in place of** y **in the original problem, it is correct.** $\dfrac{8}{4} = 2$

Solve the problems below.

1. $2x = 14$

2. $\dfrac{w}{5} = 11$

3. $3h = 45$

4. $\dfrac{x}{4} = 36$

5. $\dfrac{x}{3} = 9$

6. $6d = 66$

7. $\dfrac{w}{9} = 3$

8. $7r = 98$

9. $\dfrac{y}{3} = 2$

10. $10y = 30$

11. $\dfrac{r}{4} = 7$

12. $8t = 96$

13. $\dfrac{z}{2} = 15$

14. $\dfrac{n}{9} = 5$

15. $4z = 24$

16. $6d = 84$

17. $\dfrac{t}{3} = 3$

18. $\dfrac{m}{6} = 9$

19. $9p = 72$

20. $5a = 60$

Sometimes the answer to the algebra problem is a **fraction**. Read the example below, and you will see how easy it is.

Example 5: $4x = 5$

Solve problems like this just like the problems above and those on the previous page. The only difference is that the answer is a fraction.

In this problem, the 4 is **multiplied** by x. To solve, we need to divide both sides of the equation by 4.

$4x = 5$ Now **divide** by 4. $\dfrac{4x}{4} = \dfrac{5}{4}$ Now cancel. $\dfrac{\cancel{4}x}{\cancel{4}} = \dfrac{5}{4}$ So $x = \dfrac{5}{4}$

When you put $\dfrac{5}{4}$ in place of x in the original problem, it is correct.

$4 \times \dfrac{5}{4} = 5$ Now cancel. $\longrightarrow$ $\cancel{4} \times \dfrac{5}{\cancel{4}} = 5$ So $5 = 5$

Solve the problems below. Some of the answers will be fractions. Some answers will be integers.

1. $2x = 3$

2. $4y = 5$

3. $5t = 2$

4. $12b = 144$

5. $9a = 72$

6. $8y = 16$

7. $7x = 21$

8. $4z = 64$

9. $7x = 126$

10. $6p = 10$

11. $2n = 9$

12. $5x = 11$

13. $15m = 180$

14. $5h = 21$

15. $3y = 8$

16. $2t = 10$

17. $3b = 2$

18. $5c = 14$

19. $4d = 3$

20. $5z = 75$

21. $9y = 4$

22. $7d = 12$

23. $2w = 13$

24. $9g = 81$

25. $6a = 18$

26. $2p = 16$

27. $15w = 3$

28. $5x = 13$

6.3   Multiplying and Dividing With Negative Numbers

Example 6: $-3x = 15$

In the problem, -3 is **multiplied** by x. To find the solution, we must do the opposite. The opposite of **multiply** is **divide**. We must divide both sides of the equation by -3.

$\dfrac{-3x}{-3} = \dfrac{15}{-3}$ Then cancel. $\dfrac{\cancel{-3}x}{\cancel{-3}} = \dfrac{\overset{5}{\cancel{15}}}{\underset{1}{\cancel{-3}}}$ $x = -5$

Example 7: $\dfrac{y}{-4} = -20$

In this problem, y is **divided** by -4. To find the answer, do the opposite. **Multiply** both sides by -4.

$\cancel{-4} \times \dfrac{y}{\cancel{-4}} = (-20) \times (-4)$ so $y = 80$

Example 8: $-6a = 2$

The answer to an algebra problem can also be a negative fraction.

66

$$\frac{\cancel{6}a}{\cancel{6}} = \frac{2}{-6} \quad \longleftarrow \text{reduce to get} \quad a = \frac{1}{-3} \quad \text{or} \quad -\frac{1}{3}$$

> **Note:** A negative fraction can be written several different ways.
>
> $$\frac{1}{-3} = \frac{-1}{3} = -\frac{1}{3} = -\left(\frac{1}{3}\right)$$
>
> **All mean the same thing**

Solve the problems below. Reduce any fractions to lowest terms.

1. $2z = -6$

2. $\dfrac{y}{-5} = 20$

3. $-6k = 54$

4. $4x = -24$

5. $\dfrac{t}{7} = -4$

6. $\dfrac{r}{-2} = -10$

7. $9x = 72$

8. $\dfrac{x}{-6} = 3$

9. $\dfrac{w}{-11} = 5$

10. $5y = -35$

11. $\dfrac{x}{-4} = -9$

12. $7t = -49$

13. $-14x = -28$

14. $\dfrac{m}{3} = -12$

15. $\dfrac{c}{-6} = -6$

16. $\dfrac{d}{8} = -7$

17. $\dfrac{y}{-9} = -4$

18. $-15w = -60$

19. $-12v = 36$

20. $-8z = 32$

21. $-4x = -3$

22. $-12y = 7$

23. $\dfrac{a}{-2} = 22$

24. $-18b = 6$

25. $13a = -36$

26. $\dfrac{b}{-2} = -14$

27. $-24x = -6$

28. $\dfrac{y}{-9} = -6$

29. $\dfrac{x}{-23} = -1$

30. $7x = -7$

31. $-9y = -1$

32. $\dfrac{d}{5} = -10$

33. $\dfrac{z}{-13} = -2$

34. $-5c = 45$

35. $2d = -3$

36. $-8d = -12$

37. $-24w = 9$

38. $-6p = 42$

39. $-9a = -18$

40. $\dfrac{p}{-2} = 15$

6.4 Variables With A Coefficient of Negative One

The answer to an algebra problem should not have a negative sign in front of the variable. For example, the problem $-x = 5$ is not completely solved. Study the examples below to learn how to finish solving this problem.

Example 9: $\qquad -x = 5$

$\qquad\qquad -x$ means the same thing as $-1x$ or -1 times x. To solve this problem, **multiply** both sides by -1.

$$(-1)(-1x) = (-1)(5) \qquad \text{so } x = -5$$

Example 10: $\quad -y = -3 \quad$ Solve the same way.
$$(-1)(-y) = (-1)(-3) \qquad \text{so } y = 3$$

Solve the following problems.

1. $-w = 14$ 4. $-x = -25$ 7. $-p = -34$ 10. $-v = -9$

2. $-a = 20$ 5. $-y = -16$ 8. $-m = 81$ 11. $-k = 13$

3. $-x = -15$ 6. $-t = 62$ 9. $-w = 17$ 12. $-q = 7$

6.5   Graphing Inequalities

An inequality is a sentence that contains a $\neq, <, >, \leq,$ or $\geq$ sign. Look at the following graphs of inequalities on a number line.

NUMBER LINE

$x < 3$ is read "x is less than 3".

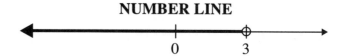

There is no line under the $<$ sign, so the graph uses an **open** endpoint to show x is less than 3 but does not include 3.

$x \leq 5$ is read "x is less than or equal to 5".

If you see a line under $<$ or $>$ ($\leq$ or $\geq$), the endpoint is filled in. The graph uses a **closed** circle because the number 5 is included in the graph.

$x > -2$ is read "x is greater than -2".

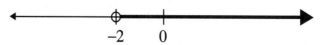

$x \geq 1$ is read "x is greater than or equal to 1".

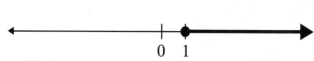

There can be more than one inequality sign. For example:

$-2 \leq x \leq 4$ is read "-2 is less than or equal to x and x is less than 4".

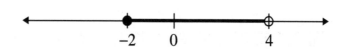

$x < 1$ or $x \geq 4$ is read "x is less than 1 or x is greater than or equal to 4".

Graph the solution sets of the following inequalities.

1. $x > 8$

6. $x < -2$ or $x > 1$

2. $x \leq 5$

7. $x \geq 10$

3. $-5 < x < 1$

8. $x < 4$

4. $x > 7$

9. $x \leq 3$ or $x \geq 5$

5. $1 \leq x < 4$

10. $x < -1$ or $x > 1$

Give the inequality represented by each of the following number lines.

11.  _____

16.  _____

12. _____

17. _____

13.  _____

18. _____

14. _____

19.  _____

15. _____

20. _____

6.6   Solving Inequalities by Addition and Subtraction

If you add or subtract the same number to both sides of an inequality, the inequality remains the same. It works just like an equation.

Example 11:   Solve and graph the solution set for $x - 2 \leq 5$.

Step 1:   Add 2 to both sides of the inequality.

$$\begin{array}{r} x - 2 \leq 5 \\ +2 \ +2 \\ \hline x \leq 7 \end{array}$$

Step 2:   Graph the solution set for the inequality.

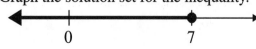

Solve and graph the solution set for the following inequalities.

1. $x + 5 > 3$

2. $x - 10 < 5$

3. $x - 2 \leq 1$

4. $9 + x \geq 7$

5. $x - 4 > -2$

6. $x + 11 \leq 20$

7. $x - 3 < -12$

8. $x + 6 \geq -3$

9. $x + 12 \leq 8$

10. $15 + x > 5$

11. $x - 6 < -2$

12. $x + 7 \geq 4$

13. $14 + x \leq 8$

14. $x - 8 > 24$

15. $x + 1 \leq 12$

16. $11 + x \geq 11$

17. $x - 3 < 17$

18. $x + 9 > -4$

19. $x + 6 \leq 14$

20. $x - 8 \geq 19$

6.7   Solving Inequalities by Multiplication and Division

If you multiply or divide both sides of an inequality by a **positive** number, the inequality symbol stays the same. However, if you multiply or divide both sides of an inequality by a **negative** number, **you must reverse the direction of the inequality symbol.**

Example 12:   Solve and graph the solution set for $4x \leq 20$.

Step 1:   Divide both sides of the inequality by 4. $\dfrac{\overset{1}{\cancel{4}}x}{\underset{1}{\cancel{4}}} \leq \dfrac{\overset{5}{\cancel{20}}}{\underset{1}{\cancel{4}}}$

Step 2:   Graph the solution. $x \leq 5$

Example 13:   Solve and graph the solution set for $6 > -\dfrac{x}{3}$.

Step 1:   Multiply both sides by -3 and **reverse the direction of the symbol.**

$$(-3) \times 6 < \dfrac{x}{\cancel{-3}} \times \cancel{-3}$$

Step 2:   Graph the solution. $-18 < x$

Solve and graph the following inequalities.

1. $\dfrac{x}{5} > 4$

2. $2x \le 24$

3. $-6x \ge 36$

4. $\dfrac{x}{10} > -2$

5. $-\dfrac{x}{4} > 8$

6. $-7x \le -49$

7. $-3x > 18$

8. $-\dfrac{x}{7} \ge 9$

9. $9x \le 54$

10. $\dfrac{x}{8} > 1$

11. $-\dfrac{x}{9} \le 3$

12. $-4x < -12$

13. $-\dfrac{x}{2} \ge -20$

14. $10x \le 30$

15. $\dfrac{x}{12} > -4$

16. $-6x < 24$

Chapter 6 Review

Solve the following one-step algebra problems.

1. $5y = -25$

2. $x + 4 = 24$

3. $d - 11 = 14$

4. $\dfrac{a}{6} = -8$

5. $-t = 2$

6. $-14b = 12$

7. $\dfrac{c}{-10} = -3$

8. $z - 15 = -19$

9. $-13d = 4$

10. $\dfrac{x}{-14} = 2$

11. $-4k = -12$

12. $y + 13 = 27$

13. $15 + h = 4$

14. $14p = 2$

15. $\dfrac{b}{4} = 11$

16. $p - 26 = 12$

17. $x + (-2) = 5$

18. $m + 17 = 27$

19. $\dfrac{k}{-4} = 13$

20. $-18a = -7$

21. $21t = -7$

22. $z - (-9) = 14$

23. $23 + w = 28$

24. $n - 35 = -16$

25. $-a = 26$

26. $-19 + f = -9$

27. $\dfrac{w}{11} = 3$

28. $-7y = 28$

29. $x + 23 = 20$

30. $z - 12 = -7$

31. $-16 + g = 40$

32. $\dfrac{m}{-3} = -9$

33. $d + (-6) = 17$ 35. $k - 16 = 5$ 37. $-2z = -36$ 39. $w - 16 = 4$

34. $-p = 47$ 36. $9y = -3$ 38. $10h = 12$ 40. $y + 10 = -8$

Graph the solution sets of the following inequalities.

41. $x \leq -3$ 43. $x < -2$

42. $x > 6$ 44. $x \geq 4$

Give the inequality represented by each of the following number lines.

45. _____   47. _____

46. _____   48. _____

Solve and graph the solution set for the following inequalities.

49. $x - 2 > 8$ 55. $-\dfrac{x}{3} \leq 5$

50. $4 + x < -1$ 56. $x + 10 \leq 4$

51. $6x \geq 54$ 57. $x - 6 \geq -2$

52. $-2x \leq 8$ 58. $7x < -14$

53. $\dfrac{x}{2} > -1$ 59. $-3x > -12$

54. $-x < -9$ 60. $-\dfrac{x}{6} \leq -3$

Chapter 7
Solving Multi-Step Equations and Inequalities

7.1   Two-Step Algebra Problems

In the following two-step algebra problems, **additions** and **subtractions** are performed first and then **division**.

Example 1: $-4x + 7 = 31$

Step 1:   Subtract 7 from both sides.

$$\begin{array}{rr} -4x + 7 & = 31 \\ -7 & -7 \\ \hline -4x & = 24 \end{array}$$

Step 2:   Divide both sides by -4.

$$\frac{-4x}{-4} = \frac{24}{-4} \qquad \text{so } x = -6$$

Example 2: $-8 - y = 12$

Step 1:   Add 8 to both sides.

$$\begin{array}{rr} -8 - y & = 12 \\ +8 & +8 \\ \hline -y & = 20 \end{array}$$

Step 2:   To finish solving a problem with a negative sign in front of the variable, multiply both sides by -1. The variable needs to be positive in the answer.

$$(-1)(-y) = (-1)(20) \text{ so } y = -20$$

Solve the two-step algebra problems below.

1. $6x - 4 = -34$

2. $5y - 3 = 32$

3. $8 - t = 1$

4. $10p - 6 = -36$

5. $11 - 9m = -70$

6. $4x - 12 = 24$

7. $3x - 17 = -41$

8. $9d - 5 = 49$

9. $10h + 8 = 78$

10. $-6b - 8 = 10$

11. $-g - 24 = -17$

12. $-7k - 12 = 30$

13. $9 - 5r = 64$

14. $6y - 14 = 34$

15. $12f + 15 = 51$

16. $21t + 17 = 80$

17. $20y + 9 = 149$

18. $15p - 27 = 33$

19. $22h + 9 = 97$

20. $-5 + 36w = 175$

7.2   Two-Step Algebra Problems With Fractions

An algebra problem may contain a fraction. Study the following example to understand how to solve algebra problems that contain a fraction.

Example 3: $\dfrac{x}{2} + 4 = 3$

Step 1: $\dfrac{x}{2} + 4 = 3$ Subtract 4 from both sides.

$$\dfrac{-4 \qquad -4}{\dfrac{x}{2} \qquad\quad = -1}$$

Step 2: $\dfrac{x}{2} = 1$, this looks like the one-step algebra problems you solved in the previous chapter.

$$\dfrac{x}{2} \times 2 = -1 \times 2, \; x = -2$$

Simplify the following algebra problems.

1. $4 + \dfrac{y}{3} = 7$

2. $\dfrac{a}{2} + 5 = 12$

3. $\dfrac{w}{5} - 3 = 6$

4. $\dfrac{x}{9} - 9 = -5$

5. $\dfrac{b}{6} + 2 = -4$

6. $7 + \dfrac{z}{2} = -13$

7. $\dfrac{x}{2} - 7 = 3$

8. $\dfrac{c}{5} + 6 = -2$

9. $3 + \dfrac{x}{11} = 7$

10. $16 + \dfrac{m}{6} = 14$

11. $\dfrac{p}{3} + 5 = -2$

12. $\dfrac{t}{8} + 9 = 3$

13. $\dfrac{v}{7} - 8 = -1$

14. $5 + \dfrac{h}{10} = 8$

15. $\dfrac{k}{7} - 9 = 1$

16. $\dfrac{y}{4} + 13 = 8$

17. $15 + \dfrac{z}{14} = 13$

18. $\dfrac{b}{6} - 9 = -14$

19. $\dfrac{d}{3} + 7 = 12$

20. $10 + \dfrac{b}{6} = 4$

21. $2 + \dfrac{p}{4} = -6$

22. $\dfrac{t}{7} - 9 = -5$

23. $\dfrac{a}{10} - 1 = 3$

24. $\dfrac{a}{8} + 16 = 9$

7.3   More Two-Step Algebra Problems With Fractions

Study the following example to understand how to solve algebra problems that contain a different type of fraction.

Example 4: $\dfrac{x+2}{4} = 3$ In this example, "$x+2$" is divided by 4, and not just the x or the 2

Step 1: $\dfrac{x+2}{4} \times 4 = 3 \times 4$ First multiply both sides by 4 to eliminate the fraction.

Step 2:
$$\begin{aligned} x+2 &= 12 \\ -2 \quad &\quad -2 \\ \hline x &= 10 \end{aligned}$$
Next, subtract 2 from both sides.

Solve the following problems.

1. $\dfrac{x+1}{5} = 4$

2. $\dfrac{z-9}{2} = 7$

3. $\dfrac{b-4}{4} = -5$

4. $\dfrac{y-9}{3} = 7$

5. $\dfrac{d-10}{-2} = 12$

6. $\dfrac{w-10}{-8} = -4$

7. $\dfrac{x-1}{-2} = -5$

8. $\dfrac{c+40}{-5} = -7$

9. $\dfrac{13+h}{2} = 12$

10. $\dfrac{k-10}{3} = 9$

11. $\dfrac{a+11}{-4} = 4$

12. $\dfrac{x-20}{7} = 6$

13. $\dfrac{t+2}{6} = -5$

14. $\dfrac{b+1}{-7} = 2$

15. $\dfrac{f-9}{3} = 8$

16. $\dfrac{4+w}{6} = -6$

17. $\dfrac{3+t}{3} = 10$

18. $\dfrac{x+5}{5} = -3$

19. $\dfrac{g+3}{2} = 11$

20. $\dfrac{k+1}{-6} = 5$

21. $\dfrac{y-14}{2} = -8$

22. $\dfrac{z-4}{-2} = 13$

23. $\dfrac{w+2}{15} = -1$

24. $\dfrac{3+h}{3} = 6$

7.4   Rationalizing the Denominator

As we have seen, algebra problems can contain fractions. The problems can contain many different types of fractions. In this section, the algebra problems will have a fraction that contains a variable as the denominator. In other words, a the bottom number of a fraction can be a variable in algebra problems.

Example 5:   Solve $\dfrac{1}{x} + 5 = 7$ for x.

Step 1:   The first thing to do is get all of the constants on one side of the equation. Do this by subtracting both sides by 5.
$$\dfrac{1}{x} + 5 - 5 = 7 - 5$$
$$\dfrac{1}{x} + 0 = 2$$
$$\dfrac{1}{x} = 2$$

Step 2:   Next, multiply both sides of the equation by x to get x out the denominator of the fraction.
$$\dfrac{1}{x} \times x = 2 \times x$$
$$1 = 2x$$

Step 3:   Last, divide both sides by 2 to get x on one side of the equation by itself.
$$\dfrac{1}{2} = \dfrac{2x}{2}$$
$$\dfrac{1}{2} = x \text{ or } x = \dfrac{1}{2}$$

Solve the following problems.

1. $\dfrac{4}{x} - 3 = 1$

2. $3 + \dfrac{2}{t} = 6$

3. $\dfrac{5}{p} + 5 = -10$

4. $\dfrac{12}{x} - 1 = 2$

5. $\dfrac{1}{2} = 2 + \dfrac{6}{n}$

6. $\dfrac{1}{x} - 15 = -9$

7. $23 - \dfrac{9}{f} = 5$

8. $\dfrac{-2}{a} + 7 = -3$

9. $-1 = 1 + \dfrac{8}{x}$

10. $12 = \dfrac{-18}{w} + 6$

11. $17 - \dfrac{2}{x} = 25$

12. $\dfrac{100}{z} - 13 = 7$

13. $25 - \dfrac{18}{t} = -11$

14. $\dfrac{1}{d} + 7 = 6$

15. $39 - \dfrac{7}{k} = -10$

7.5   Combining Like Terms

In an algebra problem, separate **terms** by $+$ and $-$ signs. The expression $5x - 4 - 3x + 7$ has 4 terms: $5x$, 4, $3x$, and 7. Terms having the same variable can be combined (added or subtracted) to simplify the expression. $5x - 4 - 3x + 7$ simplifies to $2x + 3$.

$$5x - 3x \quad - 4 + 7$$

Simplify the following expressions.

1. $7x + 12x$

2. $8y - 5y + 8$

3. $4 - 2x + 9$

4. $11a - 16 - a$

5. $9w + 3w + 3$

6. $-5x + x + 2x$

7. $w - 15 + 9w$

8. $21 - 10t + 9 - 2t$

9. $-3 + x - 4x + 9$

10. $7b + 12 + 4b$

11. $4h - h + 2 - 5$

12. $-6k + 10 - 4k$

13. $2a + 12a - 5 + a$

14. $5 + 9c - 10$

15. $-d + 1 + 2d - 4$

16. $-8 + 4h + 1 - h$

17. $12x - 4x + 7$

18. $10 + 3z + z - 5$

19. $14 + 3y - y - 2$

20. $11p - 4 + p$

21. $11m + 2 - m + 1$

7.6 Solving Equations With Like Terms

When an equation has two or more like terms on the same side of the equation, combine like terms should be combined as the **first** step in solving the equation.

Example 6: $7x + 2x - 7 = 21 + 8$

Step 1: Combine like terms on both sides of the equation.

$$
\begin{aligned}
7x + 2x - 7 &= 21 + 8 \\
9x - 7 &= 29 \\
+7 \quad &\quad +7 \\
9x \div 9 &= 36 \div 9 \\
x &= 4
\end{aligned}
$$

Step 2: Solve the two-step algebra problem as explained previously.

Solve the equations below combining like terms first.

1. $3w - 2w + 4 = 6$

2. $7x + 3 + x = 16 + 3$

3. $5 - 6y + 9y = -15 + 5$

4. $-14 + 7a + 2a = -5$

5. $-2t + 4t - 7 = 9$

6. $9d + d - 3d = 14$

7. $-6c - 4 - 5c = 10 + 8$

8. $15m - 9 - 6m = 9$

9. $-4 - 3x - x = -16$

10. $9 - 12p + 5p = 14 + 2$

11. $10y + 4 - 7y = -17$

12. $-8a - 15 - 4a = 9$

If the equation has like terms on both sides of the equation, you must get all of the terms with a **variable** on one side of the equation and all of the **integers** on the other side of the equation.

Example 7: $3x + 2 = 6x - 1$

> **Step 1:**   Subtract $6x$ from both sides to move all the **variables** to the left side.
>
> **Step 2:**   Subtract 2 from both sides to move all the **integers** to the right side.
>
> **Step 3:**   Divide by -3 to solve for x.

$$\begin{aligned} 3x + 2 &= 6x - 1 \\ -6x &\quad -6x \\ \hline -3x + 2 &= -1 \\ -2 &\quad -2 \\ \hline \frac{-3x}{-3} &= \frac{-3}{-3} \\ x &= 1 \end{aligned}$$

Solve the following problems.

1. $3a + 1 = a + 9$

2. $2d - 12 = d + 3$

3. $5x + 6 = 14 - 3x$

4. $15 - 4y = 2y - 3$

5. $9w - 7 = 12w - 13$

6. $10b + 19 = 4b - 5$

7. $-7m + 9 = 29 - 2m$

8. $5x - 26 = 13x - 2$

9. $19 - p = 3p - 9$

10. $-7p - 14 = -2p + 11$

11. $16y + 12 = 9y + 33$

12. $13 - 11w = 3 - w$

13. $-17b + 23 = -4 - 8b$

14. $k + 5 = 20 - 2k$

15. $12 + m = 4m + 21$

16. $7p - 30 = p + 6$

17. $19 - 13z = 9 - 12z$

18. $8y - 2 = 4y + 22$

19. $5 + 16w = 6w - 45$

20. $-27 - 7x = 2x + 18$

21. $-12x + 14 = 8x - 46$

22. $27 - 11h = 5 - 9h$

23. $5t + 36 = -6 - 2t$

24. $17y + 42 = 10y + 7$

25. $22x - 24 = 14x - 8$

26. $p - 1 = 4p + 17$

27. $4d + 14 = 3d - 1$

28. $7w - 5 = 8w + 12$

29. $-3y - 2 = 9y + 22$

30. $17 - 9m = m - 23$

7.7   Multi-Step Algebra Problems

You can now use what you know about removing parentheses, combining like terms, and solving simple algebra problems to solve problems that involve three or more steps. Study the examples below to see how easy it is to solve multi-step problems.

Example 8: $3(x+6) = 5x - 2$

Step 1:   Use the distributive property to remove parentheses.

$$3x + 18 = 5x - 2$$

Step 2:   Subtract $5x$ from each side to move the terms with variables to the left side of the equation.

$$\frac{-5x \qquad -5x}{-2x + 18 = -2}$$

Step 3:   Subtract 18 from each side to move the integers to the right side of the equation.

$$\frac{-18 \qquad -18}{\frac{-2x}{-2} = \frac{-20}{-2}}$$

Step 4:   Divide both sides by -2 to solve for x.

$$x = 10$$

Example 9: $\dfrac{3(x-3)}{2} = 9$

Step 1:   Use the distributive property to remove parentheses.

$$\frac{3x - 9}{2} = 9$$

Step 2:   Multiply both sides by 2 to eliminate the fraction.

$$\frac{\cancel{2}(3x-9)}{\cancel{2}} \qquad 2(9)$$
$$3x - 9 = 18$$

Step 3:   Add 9 to both sides, and combine like terms.

$$\frac{+9 \qquad +9}{\frac{3x}{3} = \frac{27}{3}}$$

Step 4:   Divide both sides by 3 to solve for x.

$$x = 9$$

Solve the following multi-step algebra problems.

1. $2(y-3) = 4y + 6$

2. $\dfrac{2(a+4)}{2} = 12$

3. $\dfrac{10(x-2)}{5} = 14$

4. $\dfrac{12y - 18}{6} = 4y + 3$

5. $2x + 3x = 30 - x$

6. $\dfrac{2a+1}{3} = a + 5$

7. $5(b-4) = 10b + 5$

8. $-8(y+4) = 10y + 4$

9. $\dfrac{x+4}{-3} = 6 - x$

10. $\dfrac{4\,(n+3)}{5} = n - 3$

11. $3\,(2x - 5) = 8x - 9$

12. $7 - 10a = 9 - 9a$

13. $7 - 5x = 10 - (6x + 7)$

14. $4\,(x - 3) - x = x - 6$

15. $4a + 4 = 3a - 4$

16. $-3\,(x - 4) + 5 = -2x - 2$

17. $5b - 11 = 13 - b$

18. $\dfrac{-4x + 3}{2x} = \dfrac{7}{2x}$

19. $-(x + 1) = -2\,(5 - x)$

20. $4\,(2c + 3) - 7 = 13$

21. $6 - 3a = 9 - 2\,(2a + 5)$

22. $-5x + 9 = -3x + 11$

23. $3y + 2 - 2y - 5 = 4y + 3$

24. $3y - 10 = 4 - 4y$

25. $-(a + 3) = -2\,(2a + 1) - 7$

26. $5m - 2\,(m + 1) = m - 10$

27. $\dfrac{1}{2}\,(b - 2) = 5$

28. $-3\,(b - 4) = -2b$

29. $4x + 12 = -2\,(x + 3)$

30. $\dfrac{7x + 4}{3} = 2x - 1$

31. $9x - 5 = 8x - 7$

32. $7x - 5 = 4x + 10$

33. $\dfrac{4x + 8}{2} = 6$

34. $2\,(c + 4) + 8 = 10$

35. $y - (y + 3) = y + 6$

36. $4 + x - 2\,(x - 6) = 8$

7.8 Solving Radical Equations

Some multi-step equations contain radicals. An example of a radical is a square root, $\sqrt{}$. Work these type of equations out similarly to the section on equations.

Example 10: Solve the following equation for x. $\sqrt{4x-3} + 2 = 5$

Step 1: The first step is to get the constants that are not under the radical on one side. Subtract 2 from both sides of the equation.
$$\sqrt{4x-3} + 2 - 2 = 5 - 2$$
$$\sqrt{4x-3} + 0 = 3$$
$$\sqrt{4x-3} = 3$$

Step 2: Next, you must get rid of the radical sign by squaring both sides of the equation.
$$\left(\sqrt{4x-3}\right)^2 = (3)^2$$
$$4x - 3 = 9$$

Step 3: Add 3 to both sides of the equation to get the constants on just one side of the equation.
$$4x - 3 + 3 = 9 + 3$$
$$4x + 0 = 12$$
$$4x = 12$$

Step 4: Last, get x on one side of the equation by itself by dividing both sides by 4.
$$\frac{4x}{4} = \frac{12}{4}$$
$$x = 3$$

Solve the following equations.

1. $\sqrt{x+3} - 13 = -8$

2. $3 + \sqrt{7t-3} = 5$

3. $\sqrt{3q+12} - 4 = 5$

4. $\sqrt{11f+3} + 2 = 8$

5. $5 = \sqrt{6g-5} + (-2)$

6. $-2 = \sqrt{x-3}$

7. $\sqrt{-8t} - 3 = 1$

8. $\sqrt{-d+1} - 9 = -6$

9. $10 - \sqrt{8x+2} = 9$

10. $\sqrt{15y+4} + 4 = -4$

11. $\sqrt{r+14} - 1 = 9$

12. $3 - \sqrt{2q-1} = 6$

13. $\sqrt{5t+16} + 4 = 13$

14. $17 = \sqrt{23-f} + 15$

15. $19 - \sqrt{7x-5} = 22$

7.9   Multi-Step Inequalities

Remember that adding and subtracting with inequalities follow the same rules as equations. When you multiply or divide both sides of an inequality by the same positive number, the rules are also the same as for equations. However, when you multiply or divide both sides of an inequality by a **negative** number, you must **reverse** the inequality symbol.

Example 11: $-x > 4$
$(-1)(-x) < (-1)(4)$
$x < -4$

Example 12: $-4x < 2$

$\dfrac{-4x}{-4} > \dfrac{2}{-4}$

$x > -\dfrac{1}{2}$

Reverse the symbol when you multiply or divide by a negative number.

When solving multi-step inequalities, first add and subtract to isolate the term with the variable. Then multiply and divide.

Example 13: $2x - 8 > 4x + 1$

Step 1:   Add 8 to both sides.

$2x - 8 + 8 > 4x + 1 + 8$
$2x > 4x + 9$

Step 2:   Subtract $4x$ from both sides.

$2x - 4x > 4x + 9 - 4x$
$-2x > 9$

Step 3:   Divide by -2. Remember to change the direction of the inequality sign.

$\dfrac{-2x}{-2} < \dfrac{9}{-2}$

$x > -\dfrac{9}{2}$

Solve each of the following inequalities.

1. $8 - 3x \le 7x - 2$

2. $3(2x - 5) \ge 8x - 5$

3. $\dfrac{1}{3}b - 2 > 5$

4. $7 + 3y > 2y - 5$

5. $3a + 5 < 2a - 6$

6. $3(a - 2) > -5a - 2(3 - a)$

7. $2x - 7 \ge 4(x - 3) + 3x$

8. $6x - 2 \le 5x + 5$

9. $-\dfrac{x}{4} > 12$

10. $-\dfrac{2x}{3} \le 6$

11. $3b + 5 < 2b - 8$

12. $4x - 5 \le 7x + 13$

13. $4x + 5 \le -2$

14. $2y - 5 > 7$

15. $4 + 2(3 - 2y) \le 6y - 20$

16. $-4c + 6 \le 8$

17. $-\dfrac{1}{2}x + 2 > 9$

18. $\dfrac{1}{4}y - 3 \le 1$

19. $-3x + 4 > 5$

20. $\dfrac{y}{2} - 2 \ge 10$

21. $7 + 4c < -2$

22. $2 - \dfrac{a}{2} > 1$

23. $10 + 4b \le -2$

24. $-\dfrac{1}{2}x + 3 > 4$

7.10   Solving Equations and Inequalities with Absolute Values

When solving equations and inequalities which involve variables placed in absolute values, remember that there will be two or more numbers that will work as correct answers. This is because the absolute value variable will signify both positive and negative numbers as answers.

Example 14: $5 + 3\,|k| = 8$ Solve as you would any equation.

   Step 1: $3\,|k| = 3$ Subtract 5 from each side.

   Step 2: $|k| = 1$ Divide by 3 on each side.

   Step 3: $k = 1$ or $k = -1$ Because k is an absolute value, the answer can be 1 or -1

Example 15: $2\,|x| - 3 < 7$ Solve as you normally would an inequality.

   Step 1: $2\,|x| < 10$ Add 3 to both sides.

   Step 2: $|x| < 5$ Divide by 2 on each side.

   Step 3: $x < 5$ or $x > -5$ Because x is an absolute value, the answer is a set of both
           or $-5 < x < 5$ positive and negative numbers.

Read each problem, and write the number or set of numbers which solves each equation or inequality.

1. $7 + 2\,|y| = 15$

2. $4\,|x| - 9 < 3$

3. $6\,|k| + 2 = 14$

4. $10 - 4\,|n| > -14$

5. $-3 = 5\,|z| + 12$

6. $-4 = 7\,|m| < 10$

7. $5\,|x| - 12 > 13$

8. $21\,|g| + 7 = 49$

9. $-9 + 6\,|x| = 15$

10. $12 - 6\,|w| > -12$

11. $31 > 13 + 9\,|r|$

12. $-30 = 21 - 3\,|t|$

13. $9\,|x| - 19 < 35$

14. $-13\,|c| + 21 \geq -31$

15. $5 - 11\,|k| < -17$

16. $-42 = 14\,|p| = 14$

17. $15 < 3\,|b| + 6$

18. $9 + 5\,|q| = 29$

19. $-14\,|y| - 38 < -45$

20. $36 = 4\,|s| + 20$

21. $20 \leq -60 + 8\,|e|$

7.11   More Solving Equations and Inequalities with Absolute Values

Now, look at the following examples in which numbers and variables are added or subtracted in the absolute value symbols ($||$).

Example 16: $|3x - 5| = 10$ Remember an equation with the absolute value symbols has two solutions.

Step 1: $3x - 5 = 10$ To find the first solution, remove the absolute value
$3x - 5 + 5 = 10 + 5$ symbol and solve the equation.
$\dfrac{\cancel{3}x}{\cancel{3}} = \dfrac{15}{3}$

$x = 15$

Step 2: $-(3x - 5) = 10$ To find the second solution, solve the equation for the
$-3x + 5 = 10$ negative of the expression in absolute value symbols.
$-3x + 5 - 5 = 10 - 5$
$-3x = 5$

$x = \dfrac{-5}{3}$

Solutions: $x = 5$ and $x = \dfrac{-5}{3}$

Example 17: $|5z - 10| < 20$ Remember the absolute value symbols and solve the inequality.

Step 1: $5z - 10 < 20$
$5z - 10 + 10 < 20 + 10$
$\dfrac{\cancel{5}z}{\cancel{5}} < \dfrac{30}{5}$

$z < 6$

Step 2: $-(5z - 10) < 20$ Next, solve the equation for the negative of the
$-5z + 10 < 20$ expression in absolute value symbols.
$-5z + 10 - 10 < 20 - 10$

$\dfrac{-\cancel{5}z}{\cancel{5}} < \dfrac{10}{5}$
$-z < 2$
$z > -2$

Solutions: $-2 < z < 6$

85

Example 18: $|4y + 7| - 5 > 18$

Step 1: $4y + 7 - 5 + 5 > 18 + 5$ Remove the absolute value symbols and solve the
$4y + 7 > 23$ inequality.
$4y + 7 - 7 > 23 - 7$
$4y > 16$
$y > 4$

Step 2: $-(4y + 7) - 5 > 18$ Solve the equation for the negative of the
$-4y - 7 - 5 + 5 > 18 + 5$ expression in absolute value symbols.
$-4y - 7 + 7 > 23 + 7$
$-4y > 30$
$y < -7\frac{1}{2}$

Solutions: $y > 4$ or $y < -7\frac{1}{2}$

Solve the following equations and inequalities below.

1. $-4 + |2x + 4| = 14$

2. $|4b - 7| + 3 > 12$

3. $6 + |12e + 3| < 39$

4. $-15 + |8f - 14| > 35$

5. $|-9b + 13| - 12 = 10$

6. $-25 + |7b + 11| < 35$

7. $|7w + 2| - 60 > 30$

8. $63 + |3d - 12| = 21$

9. $|-23 + 8x| - 12 > +37$

10. $|61 + 20x| + 32 > 51$

11. $|4a + 13| + 31 = 50$

12. $4 + |4k - 32| < 51$

13. $8 + |4x + 3| = 21$

14. $|28 + 7v| - 28 < 77$

15. $|62p + 31| + 43 = 136$

16. $18 - |6v + 22| < 22$

17. $12 = 4 + |42 + 10m|$

18. $53 < 18 + |12e + 31|$

19. $38 > -39 + |7j + 14|$

20. $9 = |14 + 15u| + 7$

21. $11 - |2j + 50| > 45$

22. $|35 + 6i| - 3 = 14$

23. $|26 - 8r| - 9 > 41$

24. $|25 + 6z| - 21 = 28$

25. $12 < |2t + 6| - 14$

26. $50 > |9q - 10| + 6$

27. $12 + |8v - 18| > 26$

28. $-38 + |16i - 33| = 41$

29. $|-14 = 6p| - 9 < 7$

30. $28 > |25 - 5f| - 12$

Chapter 7 Review

Solve each of the following equations.

1. $4a - 8 = 28$

2. $5 + \dfrac{x}{8} = -4$

3. $-7 + 23w = 108$

4. $\dfrac{y - 8}{6} = 7$

5. $c - 13 = 5$

6. $\dfrac{b + 9}{12} = -3$

Solve.

7. $19 - 8d = d - 17$

8. $\dfrac{-3}{x} + 11 = -1$

9. $7w - 8w = -4w - 30$

10. $3 - \sqrt{6 - 2x} = 4$

11. $\dfrac{12}{f} - 7 = -5$

12. $6 + 16x = -2x - 12$

13. $\sqrt{w + 11} + 14 = 15$

14. $6 - \dfrac{1}{q} = 4$

15. $\sqrt{5k + 1} - 3 = 11$

Remove parentheses.

16. $3\left(-4x + 7\right)$

17. $11\left(2y + 5\right)$

18. $6\left(8 - 9b\right)$

19. $-8\left(-2 + 3a\right)$

20. $-2\left(5c - 3\right)$

21. $-5\left(7y - 1\right)$

Solve for the variable.

22. If $3x - y = 15$, then $y =$

23. If $7a + 2b = 1$, then $b =$

Solve each of the following equations and inequalities.

24. $\dfrac{-11c - 35}{4} = 4c - 2$

25. $5 + x - 3\left(x + 4\right) = -17$

26. $4\left(2x + 3\right) \geq 2x$

27. $7 - 3x \leq 6x - 2$

28. $\dfrac{5\left(n + 4\right)}{3} = n - 8$

29. $-y > 14$

30. $2\left(3x - 1\right) \geq 3x - 7$

31. $3\left(x + 2\right) < 7x - 10$

Chapter 8
Polynomials

Polynomials are algebraic expressions which include **monomials** containing one term, **binomials** which contain two terms, and **trinomials**, which contain three terms. Expressions with more than three terms are called **polynomials**. **Terms** are separated by plus and minus signs.

EXAMPLES

Monomials	Binomials	Trinomials	Polynomials
$4f$	$4t + 9$	$x^2 + 2x + 3$	$x^3 - 3x^2 + 3x - 9$
$3x^3$	$9 - 7g$	$5x^2 - 6x - 1$	$p^4 + 2p^3 + p^2 - 5 + p9$
$4g^2$	$5x^2 + 7x$	$y^4 + 15y^2 + 100$	
2	$6x^3 - 8x$		

8.1   Adding and Subtracting Monomials

Two **monomials** are added or subtracted as long as the **variable and its exponent** are the **same**. This is called combining like terms. Use the same rules you used for adding and subtracting integers

Example 1: $4x + 5x = 9$ $\begin{array}{r} 3x^4 \\ -8x^4 \\ \hline -5x^4 \end{array}$ $2x^2 - 9x^2 = -7x^2$ $\begin{array}{r} 5y \\ +2y \\ \hline 7y \end{array}$ $6y^3 - 5y^3 = y^3$

Remember: When the integer in front of the variable is "1", it is usually not written. $1x^2$ is the same as x^2, and $-1x$ is the same as $-x$.

Add or subtract the following monomials.

1. $2x^2 + 5x^2 =$

2. $5t + 8t =$

3. $9y^3 - 2y^3 =$

4. $6g - 8g =$

5. $7y^2 + 8y^2 =$

6. $s^5 + s^5 =$

7. $-2x - 4x =$

8. $4w^2 - w^2 =$

9. $z^4 + 9z^4 =$

10. $-k + 2k =$

11. $3x^2 - 5x^2 =$

12. $9t + 2t =$

13. $-7v^3 + 10v^3 =$

14. $-2x^3 + x^3 =$

15. $10y^4 - 5y^4 =$

16. $\begin{array}{r} y^4 \\ +2y^4 \\ \hline \end{array}$

17. $\begin{array}{r} 4x^3 \\ -9x^3 \\ \hline \end{array}$

18. $\begin{array}{r} 8t^2 \\ +7t^2 \\ \hline \end{array}$

19. $\begin{array}{r} -2y \\ -4y \\ \hline \end{array}$

20. $\begin{array}{r} 5w^2 \\ +8w^2 \\ \hline \end{array}$

21. $\begin{array}{r} 11t^3 \\ -4t^3 \\ \hline \end{array}$

22. $\begin{array}{r} -5z \\ +9z \\ \hline \end{array}$

23. $\begin{array}{r} 4w^5 \\ +w^5 \\ \hline \end{array}$

24. $\begin{array}{r} 7t^3 \\ -6t^3 \\ \hline \end{array}$

25. $\begin{array}{r} 3x \\ +8x \\ \hline \end{array}$

8.2 Adding Polynomials

When adding **polynomials,** make sure the exponents and variables are the same on the terms you are combining. The easiest way is to put the terms in columns with **like exponents** under each other. Each column is added as a separate problem. Fill in the blank spots with zeros if it helps you keep the columns straight. You never carry to the next column when adding polynomials.

Example 2:   Add $3x^2 + 14$ and $5x^2 + 2x$

$$
\begin{array}{r}
3x^2 + 0x + 14 \\
(+)\, 5x^2 + 2x + 0 \\
\hline
8x^2 + 2x + 14
\end{array}
$$

Example 3: $(4x^3 - 2x) + (-x^3 - 4)$

$$
\begin{array}{r}
4x^3 - 2x + 0 \\
(+) - x^3 + 0x - 4 \\
\hline
3x^3 - 2x - 4
\end{array}
$$

Add the following polynomials.

1. $y^2 + 3y + 2$ and $2y^2 + 4$

2. $(5y^2 + 4y - 6) + (2y^2 - 5y + 8)$

3. $5x^3 - 2x^2 + 4x - 1$ and $3x^2 - x + 2$

4. $-p + 4$ and $5p^2 - 2p + 2$

5. $(w - 2) + (w^2 + 2)$

6. $4t^2 - 5t - 7$ and $8t + 2$

7. $t^4 + t + 8$ and $2t^3 + 4t - 4$

8. $(3s^3 + s^2 - 2) + (-2s^3 + 4)$

9. $(-v^2 + 7v - 8) + (4v^3 - 6v + 4)$

10. $6m^2 - 2m + 10$ and $m^2 - m - 8$

11. $-x + 4$ and $3x^2 + x - 2$

12. $(8t^2 + 3t) + (-7t^2 - t + 4)$

13. $(3p^4 + 2p^2 - 1) + (-5p^2 - p + 8)$

14. $12s^3 + 9s^2 + 2s$ and $s^3 + s^2 + s$

15. $(-9b^2 + 7b + 2) + (-b^2 + 6b + 9)$

16. $15c^2 - 11c + 5$ and $-7c^2 + 3c - 9$

17. $5c^3 + 2c^2 + 3$ and $2c^3 + 4c^2 + 1$

18. $-14x^3 + 3x^2 + 15$ and $7x^3 - 12$

19. $(-x^2 + 2x - 4) + (3x^2 - 3)$

20. $(y^2 - 11y + 10) + (-13y^2 + 5y - 4)$

21. $3d^5 - 4d^3 + 7$ and $2d^4 - 2d^3 - 2$

22. $(6t^5 - t^3 + 17) + (4t^5 + 7t^3)$

23. $4p^2 - 8p + 9$ and $-p^2 - 3p - 5$

24. $20b^3 + 15b$ and $-4b^2 - 5b + 14$

25. $(-2w + 11) + (w^3 + w - 4)$

26. $(25z^2 + 13z + 8) + (z^2 - 2z - 10)$

8.3   Subtracting Polynomials

When you subtract polynomials, it is important to remember to change all the signs in the subtracted polynomial (the subtrahend) and then add.

Example 4: $(4y^2 + 8y + 9) - (2y^2 + 6y - 4)$

Step 1:   Copy the subtraction problem into vertical form.

$$\begin{array}{r} 4y^2 + 8y + 9 \\ (-)\, 2y^2 + 6y - 4 \\ \hline \end{array}$$

Make sure you line up the terms with like exponents under each other.

Step 2:   Change the subtraction sign to addition and all the signs

$$\begin{array}{r} 4y^2 + 8y + 9 \\ (+) - 2y^2 - 6y + 4 \\ \hline \end{array}$$ of the subtracted polynomial to the opposite sign.

Subtract the following polynomials.

1. $(2x^2 + 5x + 2) - (x^2 + 3x + 1)$

2. $(8y - 4) - (4y + 3)$

3. $(11t^3 - 4t^2 + 3) - (-t^3 + 4t^2 - 5)$

4. $(-3w^2 + 9w - 5) - (-5w^2 - 5)$

5. $(6a^5 - a^3 + a) - (7a^5 + a^2 - 3a)$

6. $(14c^4 + 20c^2 + 10) - (7c^4 + 5c^2 + 12)$

7. $(5x^2 - 9x) - (-7x^2 + 4x + 8)$

8. $(12y^3 - 8y^2 - 10) - (3y^3 + y + 9)$

9. $(-3h^2 - 7h + 7) - (5h^2 + 4h + 10)$

10. $(10k^3 - 8) - (-4k^3 + k^2 + 5)$

11. $(x^2 - 5x + 9) - (6x^2 - 5x + 7)$

12. $(12p^2 + 4p) - (9p - 2)$

13. $(-2m - 8) - (6m + 2)$

14. $(13y^3 + 2y^2 - 8y) - (2y^3 + 4y^2 - 7y)$

15. $(7g + 3) - (g^2 + 4g - 5)$

16. $(-8w^3 + 4w) - (-10w^3 - 4w^2 - w)$

17. $(12x^3 + x^2 - 10) - (3x^3 + 2x^2 + 1)$

18. $(2a^2 + 2a + 2) - (-a^2 + 3a + 3)$

19. $(c + 19) - (3c^2 - 7c + 2)$

20. $(-6v^2 + 12v) - (3v^2 + 2v + 6)$

21. $(4b^3 + 3b^2 + 5) - (7b^3 - 8)$

22. $(15x^3 + 5x^2 - 4) - (4x^3 - 4x^2)$

23. $(8y^2 - 2) - (11y^2 - 2y - 3)$

24. $(-z^2 - 5z - 8) - (3z^2 - 5z + 5)$

8.4 Multiplying Monomials

When two monomials have the **same variable**, you can be multiply them. Then, add the **exponents** together. If the variable has no exponent, it is understood that the exponent is 1.

Example 5: $4x^4 \times 3x^2 = 12x^6$ $2y \times 5y^2 = 10y^3$

Multiply the following monomials.

1. $6a \times 9a^5$

8. $2d^8 \times 9d^2$

15. $8w^7 \times w$

2. $2x^6 \times 5x^3$

9. $6k^3 \times 5k^2$

16. $10s^6 \times 5s^3$

3. $4y^3 \times 3y^2$

10. $7m^5 \times m$

17. $4d^5 \times 4d^5$

4. $10t^2 \times 2t^2$

11. $11z \times 2z^7$

18. $5y^2 \times 8y^6$

5. $2p^5 \times 4p^2$

12. $3w^4 \times 6w^5$

19. $7t^{10} \times 3t^5$

6. $9b^2 \times 8b$

13. $4x^4 \times 5x^3$

20. $6p^8 \times 2p^3$

7. $3c^3 \times 3c^3$

14. $5n^2 \times 3n^3$

21. $x^3 \times 2x^3$

When problems include negative signs, follow the rules for multiplying integers.

22. $-7s^4 \times 5s^3$

29. $10d \times -8d^7$

36. $-4w \times -5w^8$

23. $-6a \times -9a^5$

30. $-3g^6 \times -2g^3$

37. $-5y^4 \times 6y^2$

24. $4x \times -x$

31. $-7s^4 \times 7s^3$

38. $9x^3 \times -7x^5$

25. $-3y^2 \times -y^3$

32. $-d^3 \times -2d$

39. $-a^4 \times -a$

26. $-5b^2 \times 3b^5$

33. $11p \times -2p^5$

40. $-7k^2 \times 3k$

27. $9c^4 \times -2c$

34. $-5x^7 \times -3x^3$

41. $-15t^2 \times -t^4$

28. $-4t^3 \times 8t^3$

35. $8z^4 \times 7z^4$

42. $3x^8 \times 9x^2$

8.5 Multiplying Monomials by Polynomials

In the chapter on solving multi-step equations, you learned to remove parentheses by multiplying the number outside the parentheses by each term inside the parentheses: $2(4x - 7) = 8x - 14$. Multiplying monomials by polynomials works the same way.

Example 6: $-5t(2t^2 - 7t + 9)$

    Step 1: Multiply $-5t \times 2t^2 = \mathbf{-10t^3}$

    Step 2: Multiply $-5t \times -7t = \mathbf{35t^2}$

    Step 3: Multiply $-5t \times 9 = \mathbf{-45t}$

    Step 4: Arrange the answers horizontally in order: $\mathbf{-10t^3 + 35t^2 - 45t}$

Remove parentheses in the following problems.

1. $3x(3x^2 + 4x - 1)$

2. $4y(y^3 - 7)$

3. $7a^2(2a^2 + 3a + 2)$

4. $-5d^3(d^2 - 5d)$

5. $2w(-4w^2 + 3w - 8)$

6. $8p(p^3 - 6p + 5)$

7. $-9b^2(-2b + 5)$

8. $2t(t^2 - 4t - 10)$

9. $10c(4c^2 + 3c - 7)$

10. $6z(2z^4 - 5z^2 - 4)$

11. $-9t^2(3t^2 + 5t + 6)$

12. $c(-3c - 5)$

13. $3p(p^3 - p^2 - 9)$

14. $-k^2(2k + 4)$

15. $-3(4m^2 - 5m + 8)$

16. $6x(-7x^3 + 10)$

17. $-w(w^2 - 4w + 7)$

18. $2y(5y^2 - y)$

19. $3d(d^5 - 7d^3 + 4)$

20. $-5t(-4t^2 - 8t + 1)$

21. $7(2w^2 - 9w + 4)$

22. $3y^2(y^2 - 11)$

23. $v^2(v^2 + 3v + 3)$

24. $8x(2x^3 + 3x + 1)$

25. $-5d(4d^2 + 7d - 2)$

26. $-k^2(-3k + 6)$

27. $3x(-x^2 - 5x + 5)$

28. $4z(4z^4 - z - 7)$

29. $-5y(9y^3 - 3)$

30. $2b^2(7b^2 + 4b + 4)$

8.6 Dividing Polynomials by Monomials

Example 7:
$$\frac{-8wx + 6x^2 - 16wx^2}{2wx}$$

Step 1: Rewrite the problem. Divide each term from the top by the denominator, $2wx$.

$$\frac{-8wx}{2wx} + \frac{6x^2}{2wx} + \frac{-16wx^2}{2wx}$$

Step 2: Simplify each term in the problem. Then combine like terms.

$$-4 + \frac{3x}{w} - 8x$$

Simplify each of the following.

1. $\dfrac{bc^2 - 8bc - 2b^2c^2}{2bc}$

2. $\dfrac{3jk^2 + 12k + 9j^2k}{3jk}$

3. $\dfrac{5x^2y - 8xy^2 + 2y^3}{2xy}$

4. $\dfrac{16st^2 + st - 12s}{4st}$

5. $\dfrac{4wx^2 + 6wx - 12w^3}{2wx}$

6. $\dfrac{cd^2 + 10cd^3 + 16c^2}{2cd}$

7. $\dfrac{y^2z^3 - 2yz - 8z^2}{-2yz^2}$

8. $\dfrac{a^2b + 2ab^2 - 14ab^3}{2a^2}$

9. $\dfrac{pr^2 + 6pr + 8p^2r^2}{2pr^2}$

10. $\dfrac{6xy^2 - 3xy + 18x^2}{-3xy}$

11. $\dfrac{6x^2y + 12xy - 24y^2}{6xy}$

12. $\dfrac{5m^2n - 10mn - 25n^2}{5mn}$

13. $\dfrac{st^2 - 10st - 16s^2t^2}{2st}$

14. $\dfrac{7jk^2 - 14jk - 63j^2}{7jk}$

8.7 Removing Parentheses and Simplifying

In the following problem, you must multiply each set of parentheses by the numbers and variables outside the parentheses, and then add the polynomials to simplify the expressions.

Example 8: $8x \left(2x^2 - 5x + 7\right) - 3x \left(4x^2 + 3x - 8\right)$

    Step 1: Multiply to remove the first set of parentheses.

$$8x \left(2x^2 - 5x + 7\right) = 16x^3 - 40x^2 + 56x$$

    Step 2: Multiply to remove the second set of parentheses.

$$-3x \left(4x^2 + 3x - 8\right) = -12x^3 - 9x^2 + 24x$$

    Step 3: Copy each polynomial in columns, making sure the terms with the same variable and exponent are under each other. Add to simplify.

$$\begin{array}{r} 16x^3 - 40x^2 + 56x \\ (+) - 12x^3 - 9x^2 + 24x \\ \hline 4x^3 - 49x^2 + 80x \end{array}$$

Remove the parentheses and simplify the following problems.

1. $4t \left(t + 7\right) + 5t \left(2t^2 - 4t + 1\right)$

2. $-5y \left(3y^2 - 5y + 3\right) - 6y \left(y^2 - 4y - 4\right)$

3. $-3 \left(3x^2 + 4x\right) + 5x \left(x^2 + 3x + 2\right)$

4. $2b \left(5b^2 - 8b - 1\right) - 3b \left(4b + 3\right)$

5. $8d^2 \left(3d + 4\right) - 7d \left(3d^2 + 4d + 5\right)$

6. $5a \left(3a^2 + 3a + 1\right) - \left(-2a^2 + 5a - 4\right)$

7. $3m \left(m + 7\right) + 8 \left(4m^2 + m + 4\right)$

8. $4c^2 \left(-6c^2 - 3c + 2\right) - 7c \left(5c^3 + 2c\right)$

9. $-8w \left(-w + 1\right) - 4w \left(3w - 5\right)$

10. $6p \left(2p^2 - 4p - 6\right) + 3p \left(p^2 + 6p + 9\right)$

8.8   Multiplying Two Binomials

When you multiply two binomials such as $(x + 6)(x - 5)$, you must multiply each term in the first binomial by each term in the second binomial. The easiest way is to use the **FOIL** method. If you can remember the word **FOIL**, it can help you keep order when you multiply. The "F" stands for **first**, "O" stands for **outside**, "I" stands for **inside**, and "L" stands for **last**.

F	**O**	**I**	**L**
FIRST	**OUTSIDE**	**INSIDE**	**LAST**
Multiply the **first** terms in each binomial	Next, multiply the **outside** terms.	Then, multiply the **inside** terms.	Last, multiply the **last** terms.

$(x + 6)(x - 5)$	$(x + 6)(x - 5)$	$(x + 6)(x - 5)$	$(x + 6)(x - 5)$
$x \times x = x^2$	$x \times -5 = -5x$	$6 \times x = 6x$	$6 \times -5 = -30$
x^2 +	$-5x$ +	$6x$ +	-30

Now just combine like terms, $6x - 5x = x$, and write your answer.
$(x + 6)(x - 5) = x^2 + x - 30$.

Note: It is customary for mathematicians to write polynomials in descending order. That means that the term with the highest-number exponent comes first in a polynomial. The next highest exponent is second and so on. When you use the **FOIL** method, the terms will always be in the customary order. You just need to combine like terms and write your answer.

1. $(y - 7)(y + 3)$

2. $(2x + 4)(x + 9)$

3. $(4b - 3)(3b - 4)$

4. $(6g + 2)(g - 9)$

5. $(7k - 5)(-4k - 3)$

6. $(8v - 2)(3v + 4)$

7. $(10p + 2)(4p + 3)$

8. $(3h - 9)(-2h - 5)$

9. $(w - 4)(w - 7)$

10. $(6x + 1)(x - 2)$

11. $(5t + 3)(2t - 1)$

12. $(4y - 9)(4y + 9)$

13. $(a + 6)(3a + 5)$

14. $(3z - 8)(z - 4)$

15. $(5c + 2)(6c + 5)$

16. $(y + 3)(y - 3)$

17. $(2w - 5)(4w + 6)$

18. $(7x + 1)(x - 4)$

19. $(6t - 9)(4t - 4)$

20. $(5b + 6)(6b + 2)$

21. $(2z + 1)(10z + 4)$

22. $(11w - 8)(w + 3)$

23. $(5d - 9)(9d + 9)$

24. $(9g + 2)(g - 2)$

25. $(4p + 7)(2p + 3)$

26. $(m + 5)(m - 5)$

27. $(8b - 8)(2b - 1)$

28. $(z + 3)(3z + 5)$

29. $(7y - 5)(y - 3)$

30. $(9x + 5)(3x - 1)$

31. $(3t + 1)(t + 10)$

32. $(2w - 9)(8w + 7)$

33. $(8s - 2)(s + 4)$

34. $(4k - 1)(8k + 9)$

35. $(h + 12)(h - 2)$

36. $(3x + 7)(7x + 3)$

37. $(2v - 6)(2v + 6)$

38. $(2x + 8)(2x - 3)$

39. $(k - 1)(6k + 12)$

40. $(3w + 11)(2w + 2)$

41. $(8y - 10)(5y - 3)$

42. $(6d + 13)(d - 1)$

43. $(7h + 3)(2h + 4)$

44. $(5n + 9)(5n - 5)$

45. $(6z + 5)(z - 8)$

46. $(4p + 5)(2p - 9)$

47. $(b + 2)(5b + 7)$

48. $(9y - 3)(8y - 7)$

8.9   Simplifying Expressions with Exponents

Example 9:   **Simplify** $(2a + 5)^2$

When you simplify an expression such as $(2a + 5)^2$, write the expression as two binomials and use FOIL to simplify.
$(2a + 5)^2 = (2a + 5)(2a + 5)$
Using FOIL we have $4a^2 + 10a + 10a + 25 = 4a^2 + 20a + 25$

Example 10:   **Simplify** $4(3a + 2)^2$

Using order of operations, we must simplify the exponent first.

$4(3a + 2)^2$

$4(3a + 2)(3a + 2)$

$4(9a^2 + 6a + 6a + 4)$

$4(9a^2 + 12a + 4)$ Now multiply by 4.

$4(9a^2 + 12a + 4) = 36a^2 + 48a + 16$

Multiply the following binomials.

1. $(y + 3)^2$

2. $2(2x + 4)^2$

3. $6(4b - 3)^2$

4. $5(6g + 2)^2$

5. $(-4k - 3)^2$

6. $3(-2h - 5)^2$

7. $-2(8v - 2)^2$

8. $(10p + 2)^2$

9. $6(-2h - 5)^2$

10. $6(w-7)^2$

11. $2(6x+1)^2$

12. $(9x+2)^2$

13. $(5t+3)^2$

14. $3(4y-9)^2$

15. $8(a+6)^2$

16. $4(3z-8)^2$

17. $3(5c+2)^2$

18. $4(3t+9)^2$

Chapter 8 Review

Simplify.

1. $3a^2 + 9a^2$

2. $(7x^2y^4)(9xy^5)$

3. $-6z^2(z+3)$

4. $(4b^2)(5b^3)$

5. $7x^2 - 9x^2$

6. $(5p-4)-(3p+2)$

7. $-5t(3t+9)^2$

8. $(3w^3y^2)(4wy^5)$

9. $3(2g+3)^2$

10. $14d^4 - 9d^4$

11. $(7w-4)(w-8)$

12. $(9x+2)(x+5)$

13. $4y(4y^2-9y+2)$

14. $(8a^4b)(2ab^3)(ab)$

15. $(5w^6)(9w^9)$

16. $8w^3 + 12x^3$

17. $15p^5 - 11p^5$

18. $(3s^4t^2)(4st^3)$

19. $(4d+9)(2d+7)$

20. $4w(-3w^2+7w-5)$

21. $24z^6 - 10z^6$

22. $-7y^3 - 8y^3$

23. $(a^2v)(2av)(a^3v^6)$

24. $4(6y-5)^2$

25. $(4x^5y^3)(2xy^3)$

26. $24z^6 - 10z^6$

27. $(3p^3-1)(p+5)$

28. $2b(b-4)-(b^2+2b+1)$

29. $(6k^2+5k)+(k^2+k+9)$

30. $(q^2r^3)(3qr^2)(2q^4r)$

Chapter 9
Factoring

In a multiplication problem, the numbers multiplied together are called **factors**. The answer to a multiplication problem is a called the **product**.

In the multiplication problem $5 \times 4 = 20$, 5 and 4 are factors and 20 is the product.

If we reverse the problem, $20 = 5 \times 4$, we say we have **factored** 20 into 5×4.

In this chapter, we will factor **polynomials**.

Example 1:   Find the greatest common factor of $2y^3 + 6y^2$.

    Step 1:   Look at the whole numbers. The greatest common factor of 2 and 6 is 2. Factor the 2 out of each term.

$$3\left(y^3 + 3y^2\right)$$

    Step 2:   Look at the remaining terms, $y^3 + 3y^2$. What are the common factors of each term?

$$
\begin{array}{ccccccc}
y^3 & = & y & \times & \boxed{y & \times & y} \\
3y^2 & = & 3 & \times & \boxed{y & \times & y}
\end{array}
\longleftarrow \text{ common factors } = y^2
$$

    Step 2:   Factor 2 and y^2 out of each term: $2y^2\left(y + 3\right)$

    Check: $2y^2\left(y + 3\right) = 2y^3 + 6y^2$

Find the greatest common factor of each of the following.

1. $6x^4 + 18x^2$ 6. $6x^4 - 12x^2$ 11. $27m^3 + 18m^4$ 16. $16x^2 - 24x^5$

2. $14y^3 + 7y$ 7. $18y^2 - 12y$ 12. $100x^4 - 25x^3$ 17. $15a^4 - 25a^2$

3. $4b^5 + 12b^3$ 8. $15a^3 - 25a^2$ 13. $4b^4 - 12b^3$ 18. $24b^3 + 16b^6$

4. $10a^3 + 5$ 9. $4x^3 + 16x^2$ 14. $18c^2 + 24c$ 19. $36y^4 + 9y^2$

5. $2y^3 + 8y^2$ 10. $6b^2 + 21b^5$ 15. $20y^3 + 30y^5$ 20. $42x^3 + 49x$

Factoring larger polynomials with 3 or 4 terms works the same way.

Example 2: $4x^5 + 16x^4 + 12x^3 + 8x^2$

Step 1: Find the greatest common factor of the whole numbers. 4 can be divided evenly into 4, 16, 12, and 8; therefore, 4 is the greatest common factor.

Step 2: Find the greatest common factor of the variables. x^5, x^4, x^3, and x^2 can be divided by x^2, the lowest power of x in each term.

$$4x^5 + 16x^4 + 12x^3 + 8x^2 = 4x^2 \left(x^3 + 4x^2 + 3x + 2 \right)$$

Factor each of the following polynomials.

1. $5a^3 + 15a^2 + 20a$

2. $18y^4 + 6y^3 + 24y^2$

3. $12x^5 + 21x^3 + x^2$

4. $6b^4 + 3b^3 + 15b^2$

5. $14c^3 + 28c^2 + 7c$

6. $15b^4 - 5b^2 + 20b$

7. $t^3 + 3t^2 - 5t$

8. $8a^3 - 4a^2 + 12a$

9. $16b^5 - 12b^4 - 10b^2$

10. $20x^4 + 16x^3 - 24x^2 + 28x$

11. $40b^7 + 30b^5 - 50b^3$

12. $20y^4 - 15y^3 + 30y^2$

13. $4m^5 + 8m^4 + 12m^3 + 6m^2$

14. $16x^5 + 20x^4 - 12x^3 + 24x^2$

15. $18y^4 + 21y^3 - 9y^2$

16. $3n^5 + 9n^3 + 12n^2 + 15n$

17. $4d^6 - 8d^2 + 2d$

18. $10w^2 + 4w + 2$

19. $6t^3 - 3t^2 + 9t$

20. $25p^5 - 10p^3 - 5p^2$

21. $18x^4 + 9x^2 - 36x$

22. $6b^4 - 12b^2 - 6b$

23. $y^3 + 3y^2 - 9y$

24. $10x^5 - 2x^4 + 4x^2$

Find the greatest common factor of $4a^3b^2 - 6a^2b^2 + 2a^4b^3$

Step 1:   The greatest common factor of the whole numbers is 2.

$$4a^3b^2 - 6a^2b^2 + 2a^4b^3 = 2\left(2a^3b^2 - 3a^2b^2 + a^4b^3\right)$$

Step 2:   Find the lowest power of each variable that is in each term. Factor them out of each term. The lowest power of a is a^2. The lowest power of b is b^2.

$$4a^3b^2 - 6a^2b^2 + 2a^4b^3 = 2a^2b^2\left(2a - 3 + a^2b\right)$$

Factor each of the following polynomials.

1. $3a^2b^2 - 6a^3b^4 + 9a^2b^3$

2. $12x^4y^3 + 18x^3y^4 - 24x^3y^3$

3. $20x^2y - 25x^3y^3$

4. $12x^2y - 20x^2y^2 + 16xy^2$

5. $8a^3b + 12a^2b + 20a^2b^3$

6. $36c^4 + 42c^3 + 24c^2 - 18c$

7. $14m^3n^4 - 28m^3n^2 + 42m^2n^3$

8. $16x^4y^2 - 24x^3y^2 + 12x^2y^2 - 8xy^2$

9. $32c^3d^4 - 56c^2d^3 + 64c^3d^2$

10. $21a^4b^3 + 27a^2b^3 + 15a^3b^2$

11. $4w^3t^2 + 6w^2t - 8wt^2$

12. $5pw^3 - 2p^2q^2 - 9p^3q$

13. $49x^3t^3 + 7xt^2 - 14xt^3$

14. $9cd^4 - 3d^4 - 6c^2d^3$

15. $12a^2b^3 - 14ab + 10ab^2$

16. $25x^4 + 10x - 20x^2$

17. $bx^3 - b^2x^2 + b^3x$

18. $4k^3a^2 + 22ka + 16k^2a^2$

19. $33w^4y^2 - 9w^3y^2 + 24w^2y^2$

20. $18x^3 - 9x^5 + 27x^2$

9.1   Factor By Grouping

Not all polynomials have a common factor in each term. In this case they may sometimes be factored by grouping.

Example 3:   Factor $ab + 4a + 2b + 8$

Step 1:   Factor an a from the first two terms and a 2 from the last two terms.

$$a(b + 4) + 2(b + 4)$$

Now the polynomial has two terms, $a(b + 4)$ and $2(b + 4)$. Notice that $(b + 4)$ is a factor of each term.

Step 2:   Factor out the common factor of each term:

$$ab + 4a + 2b + 8 = (b + 4)(a + 2).$$

Check: Multiply using the FOIL method to check.

$$(b + 4)(a + 2) = ab + 4a + 2b + 8$$

Factor the following polynomials by grouping.

1. $xy + 4x + 2y + 8$

2. $cd + 5c + 4d + 20$

3. $xy - 4x + 6y - 24$

4. $ab + 6a + 3b + 18$

5. $ab + 3a - 5b - 15$

6. $xy - 2x + 6x - 12$

7. $cd + 4c + 4d + 16$

8. $mn - 5m + 3n - 15$

9. $ab + 4a + 3b + 12$

10. $xy + 7x - 4y - 28$

11. $ab - 2a + 8b - 16$

12. $cd + 4c - 5d - 20$

13. $mn + 6m - 2n - 12$

14. $xy - 9x - 3y + 27$

15. $bc - 3b + 5c - 15$

16. $ab + a + 7b + 7$

17. $xy + 4y + 2y + 8$

18. $cd + 9c - d - 9$

19. $ab + 2a - 7b - 14$

20. $xy - 6x - 2y + 12$

21. $wz + 6z - 4w - 24$

9.2   Factoring Trinomials

In the chapter on polynomials, you multiplied binomials (two terms) together, and the answer was a trinomial (three terms).

For example, $(x + 6)(x - 5) = x^2 + x - 30$

Now, you need to practice factoring a trinomial into two binomials.

Example 4:   Factor $x^2 + 6x + 8$

Step 1:   When the trinomial is in descending order as in the example above, you need to find a pair of numbers whose sum equals the number in the second term, while their product equals the third term. In the above example, find the pair of numbers that has a sum of 6 and a product of 8.

$$\underline{\hspace{1cm}} + \underline{\hspace{1cm}} = 6 \quad \text{and} \quad \underline{\hspace{1cm}} \times \underline{\hspace{1cm}} = 8$$

The pair of numbers that satisfy both equations is 4 and 2.

Step 2:   Use the pair of numbers in the binomials.

The factors of $x^2 + 6x + 8$ are $(x + 4)(x + 2)$

Check: To check, use the FOIL method.
$(x + 4)(x + 2) = x^2 + 4x + 2x + 8 = x^2 + 6x + 8$

Notice, when the second term and the third term of the trinomial are both positive, both numbers in the solution are positive.

Example 5:   Factor $x^2 - x - 6$ Find the pair of numbers where:

the sum is -1 and the product is -6

$$\underline{\hspace{1cm}} + \underline{\hspace{1cm}} = -1 \quad \text{and} \quad \underline{\hspace{1cm}} \times \underline{\hspace{1cm}} = -6$$

The pair of numbers that satisfies both equations is 2 and -3.
The factors of $x^2 - x - 6$ are $(x + 2)(x - 3)$

Notice, if the second term and the third term are negative, one number in the solution pair is positive, and the other number is negative.

Example 6:   Factor $x^2 - 7x + 12$ Find the pair of numbers where:

the sum is -7 and the product is 12

$$\underline{\hspace{1cm}} + \underline{\hspace{1cm}} = -7 \quad \text{and} \quad \underline{\hspace{1cm}} \times \underline{\hspace{1cm}} = 12$$

The pair of numbers that satisfies both equations is -3 and -4
The factors of $x^2 - 7x + 12$ are $(x - 3)(x - 4)$.

Notice, if the second term of a trinomial is negative and the third term is positive, both numbers in the solution are negative.

Find the factors of the following trinomials.

1. $x^2 - x - 2$

2. $y^2 + y - 6$

3. $w^2 + 3w - 4$

4. $t^2 + 5t + 6$

5. $x^2 + 2x - 8$

6. $k^2 - 4k + 3$

7. $t^2 + 3t - 10$

8. $x^2 - 3x - 4$

9. $y^2 - 5y + 6$

10. $y^2 + y - 20$

11. $a^2 - a - 6$

12. $b^2 - 4b - 5$

13. $c^2 - 5c - 14$

14. $c^2 - c - 12$

15. $d^2 + d - 6$

16. $x^2 - 3x - 28$

17. $y^2 + 3y - 18$

18. $a^2 - 9a + 20$

19. $b^2 - 2b - 15$

20. $c^2 + 7c - 8$

21. $t^2 - 11t + 30$

22. $w^2 + 13w + 36$

23. $m^2 - 2m - 48$

24. $y^2 + 14y + 49$

25. $x^2 + 7x + 10$

26. $a^2 - 7a + 6$

27. $d^2 - 6d - 27$

9.3 More Factoring Trinomials

Sometimes a trinomial has a greatest common factor which must be factored out first.

Example 7: Factor $4x^2 + 8x - 32$

Step 1: Begin by factoring out the greatest common factor, 4.

$$4 \left(x^2 + 2x - 8 \right)$$

Step 2: Factor by finding a pair of numbers whose sum is 2 and product is -8. 4 and -2 will work, so

$$4 \left(x^2 + 2x - 8 \right) = 4 \left(x + 4 \right) \left(x - 2 \right)$$

Check: Multiply to check. $4 \left(x + 4 \right) \left(x - 2 \right) = 4x^2 + 8x - 32$

Factor the following trinomials. Be sure to factor out the greatest common factor first.

1. $2x^2 + 6x + 4$

2. $3y^2 - 9y + 6$

3. $2a^2 + 2a - 12$

4. $4b^2 + 28b + 40$

5. $3y^2 - 6y - 9$

6. $10x^2 + 10x - 200$

7. $5c^2 - 10c - 40$

8. $6d^2 + 30d - 36$

9. $4x^2 + 8x - 60$

10. $6a^2 - 18a - 24$

11. $5b^2 + 40b + 75$

12. $3c^2 - 6c - 24$

13. $2x^2 - 18x + 28$

14. $4y^2 - 20y + 16$

15. $7a^2 - 7a - 42$

16. $6b^2 - 18b - 60$

17. $11d^2 + 66d + 88$

18. $3x^2 - 24x + 45$

9.4   Factoring More Trinomials

Some trinomials have a whole number in front of the first term that cannot be factored out of the trinomial. The trinomial can still be factored.

Example 8:   Factor $2x^2 + 5x - 3$

Step 1:   To get a product of $2x^2$, one factor must begin with $2x$ and the other with x.

$(2x \qquad)(x \qquad)$

Step 2:   Now think: What two numbers give a product of -3? The two possibilities are 3 and -1 or -3 and 1. We know they could be in any order so there are 4 possible arrangements.

$(2x + 3)(x - 1)$
$(2x - 3)(x + 1)$
$(2x + 1)(x - 3)$
$(2x - 1)(x + 3)$

Step 3:   Multiply each possible answer until you find the arrangement of the numbers that works. Multiply the outside terms and the inside terms and add them together to see which one will equal $5x$.

$(2x + 3)(x - 1) = 2x^2 + x - 3$
$(2x - 3)(x + 1) = 2x^2 - x - 3$
$(2x + 1)(x - 3) = 2x^2 - 5 - 3$
$\boxed{(2x - 1)(x + 3) = 2x^2 + 5x - 3}$ $\longleftarrow$ This arrangement works, therefore:

The factors of $2x^2 + 5x - 3$ are $(2x - 1)(x + 3)$

Alternative: You can do some of the multiplying in your head. For the above example, ask yourself the following question: What two numbers give a product of -3 and give a sum of 5 (the whole number in the second term) when one number is first multiplied by 2 (the whole number in front of the first term)? The pair of numbers, -1 and 3, have a product of -3 and a sum of 5 when the 3 is first multiplied by 2. Therefore, the 3 will go opposite the factor with the $2x$ so that when the terms are multiplied, you get -5.

You can use this method to at least narrow down the possible pairs of numbers when you have several from which to choose.

Factor the following trinomials.

1. $3y^2 + 14y + 8$	10. $3a^2 + 4a - 7$	19. $5b^2 + 24b - 5$
2. $5a^2 + 24a - 5$	11. $2a^2 + 3a - 20$	20. $7d^2 + 18d + 8$
3. $7b^2 + 30b + 8$	12. $5b^2 - 13b - 6$	21. $3x^2 - 20x + 25$
4. $2c^2 - 9c + 9$	13. $3y^2 - 17x + 36$	22. $2a^2 - 7a - 4$
5. $2y^2 - 7y - 15$	14. $2x^2 - 17x + 36$	23. $5m^2 + 12m + 4$
6. $3x^2 + 4x + 1$	15. $11x^2 - 29x - 12$	24. $9y^2 - 5y - 4$
7. $7y^2 + 13y - 2$	16. $5c^2 + 2c - 16$	25. $2b^2 - 13b + 18$
8. $11a^2 + 35a + 6$	17. $7y^2 - 30y + 27$	26. $7x^2 + 31x - 20$
9. $5y^2 + 17y - 12$	18. $2x^2 - 3x - 20$	27. $3c^2 - 2c - 21$

9.5   Factoring Trinomials With Two Variables

Some trinomials have two variables with exponents. You can still factor these trinomials.

Example 9:   Factor $x^2 + 5xy + 6y^2$

Step 1:   Notice there is an x^2 in the first term and a y^2 in the last term. When you see two different terms that are squared, you know there has to be an x and a y in each factor:

$(x \quad y)(x \quad y)$

Step 2:   Now think: What are two numbers whose sum is 5 and product is 6? You see that 3 and 2 will work. Put 3 and 2 in the factors:

$$(x + 3y)(x + 2y)$$

Check: Multiply to check. $(x + 3y)(x + 2y) = x^2 + 3xy + 2xy + 6y^2 = x^2 + 5xy + 6y^2$

Factor the following trinomials.

1. $a^2 + 6ab + 8b^2$

7. $x^2 + 5xy - 24y^2$

13. $x^2 + 12xy + 32y^2$

2. $x^2 + 3xy - 4y^2$

8. $a^2 - 4ab + 4b^2$

14. $c^2 + 3cd - 40d^2$

3. $c^2 - 2cd - 15d^2$

9. $c^2 - 11cd + 30d^2$

15. $x^2 + 6xy - 27y^2$

4. $g^2 + 7gh + 10h^2$

10. $x^2 - 6xy + 8y^2$

16. $a^2 - 2ab - 48b^2$

5. $a^2 - 5ab + 6b^2$

11. $g^2 - gh - 42h^2$

17. $c^2 - 3cd - 28d^2$

6. $c^2 - cd - 30d^2$

12. $a^2 - ab - 20b^2$

18. $x^2 + xy - 6y^2$

9.6   Factoring the Difference of Two Squares

The product of a term and itself is called a **perfect square**.

25 is a perfect square because $5 \times 5 = 25$
49 is a perfect square because $7 \times 7 = 49$

Any variable with an even exponent is a perfect square.

y^2 is a perfect square because $y \times y = y^2$

y^4 is a perfect square because $y^2 \times y^2 = y^4$

When two terms that are both perfect squares are subtracted, factoring those terms is very easy. To factor the difference of perfect squares, you use the square root of each term, a plus sign in the first factor, and a minus sign in the second factor.

Example 10:   Factor $4x^2 - 9$ This example has two terms which are both perfect squares, and the terms are subtracted.

Step 1: $(2x \quad 3)(2x \quad 3)$ Find the square root of each term. Use the square roots in each of the factors.

Step 2: $(2x + 3)(2x - 3)$ Use a plus sign in one factor and a minus sign in the other factor.

Check: Multiply to check. $(2x + 3)(2x - 3) = 4x^2 - 6x + 6x - 9 = 4x^2 - 9$

The inner and outer terms add to zero.

Example 11:   Factor $81y^4 - 1$

Step 1: $(9y^2 + 1)(9y^2 - 1)$ Factor like the example above. Notice, the second factor is also the difference of two perfect squares.

Step 2: $(9y^2 + 1)(3y + 1)(3y - 1)$ Factor the second term further. **Note: You cannot factor the sum of two perfect squares.**

Check: Multiply in reverse to check your answer.
$(9y^2 + 1)(3y + 1)(3y - 1) = (9y^2 + 1)(9y^2 - 3y + 3y - 1) =$
$(9y^2 + 1)(9y^2 - 1) = 81y^4 + 9y^2 - 9y^2 - 1 = 81y^4 - 1$

Factor the following differences of perfect squares.

1. $64x^2 - 49$

2. $4y^4 - 25$

3. $9a^4 - 4$

4. $25c^4 - 9$

5. $64y^2 - 9$

6. $x^4 - 16$

7. $49x^2 - 4$

8. $4d^2 - 25$

9. $9a^2 - 16$

10. $100y^4 - 49$

11. $c^4 - 36$

12. $36x^2 - 25$

13. $25x^2 - 4$

14. $9x^4 - 64$

15. $49x^2 - 100$

16. $16x^2 - 81$

17. $9y^4 - 1$

18. $64c^2 - 25$

19. $25d^2 - 64$

20. $36a^4 - 49$

21. $16x^4 - 16$

22. $b^2 - 25$

23. $c^4 - 144$

24. $9y^2 - 4$

25. $81x^4 - 16$

26. $4b^2 - 36$

27. $9w^2 - 9$

28. $64a^2 - 25$

29. $49y^2 - 121$

30. $x^6 - 9$

Chapter 9 Review

Factor the following polynomials completely.

1. $8x - 18$

2. $6x^2 - 18x$

3. $16b^3 + 8b$

4. $15a^3 + 40$

5. $20y^6 - 12y^4$

6. $5a - 15a^2$

7. $4y^2 - 36$

8. $25a^4 - 49b^2$

9. $3ax + 3ay + 4x + 4y$

10. $ax - 2x + ay - 2y$

11. $2bx + 2x - 2by - 2y$

12. $2b^2 - 2b - 12$

13. $yx^3 + 14x - 3x^2 - 6$

14. $3a^3 + 4a^2 + 9a + 12$

15. $27y^2 + 42y - 5$

16. $12b^2 + 25b - 7$

17. $c^2 + cd - 20d^2$

18. $x^2 - 4xy - 21y^2$

19. $6y^2 + 30y + 36$

20. $2b^2 + 6b - 20$

21. $16b^4 - 81d^4$

22. $9w^2 - 54w - 63$

23. $m^2p^2 - 5mp + 2m^2p - 10m$

24. $12x^2 + 27x$

25. $2xy - 36 + 8y - 9x$

26. $2a^4 - 32$

27. $21c^2 + 41c + 10$

28. $x^2 - y + xy - x$

29. $2b^3 - 24 + 16b - 3b^2$

30. $5 - 2a - 25a^2 + 10a^3$

Chapter 10
Solving Quadratic Equations

In the previous chapter, we factored polynomials such as $y^2 - 4y - 5$ into two factors:

$$y^2 - 4y - 5 = (y + 1)(y - 5)$$

In this chapter, we learn that any equation that can be put in the form $ax^2 + bx + c = 0$ is a quadratic equation if a, b, and c are real numbers and $a \neq 0$. $ax^2 + bx + c = 0$ is the standard form of a quadratic equation. To solve these equations, follow the steps below.

Example 1:   Solve $y^2 - 4y - 5 = 0$

Step 1:   Factor the left side of the equation.

$$y^2 - 4y - 5 = 0$$
$$(y + 1)(y - 5) = 0$$

Step 2:   If the product of these two factors equals zero, then the two factors individually must be equal to zero. Therefore, so solve, we set each factor equal to zero.

$$
\begin{array}{ccc}
(y + 1) & = 0 & \\
\underline{-1 \quad -1} & & \\
y & = -1 &
\end{array}
\qquad
\begin{array}{ccc}
(y - 5) & = 0 & \\
\underline{+5 \quad +5} & & \\
y & = 5 &
\end{array}
$$

The equation has two solutions: $y = -1$ and $y = 5$

Check: To check, substitute each solution into the original equation.

When $y = -1$, the equation becomes:

$$
\begin{aligned}
(-1)^2 - (4)(-1) - 5 &= 0 \\
1 + 4 - 5 &= 0 \\
0 &= 0
\end{aligned}
$$

When $y = 5$, the equation becomes:

$$
\begin{aligned}
5^2 - (4)(5) - 5 &= 0 \\
25 - 20 - 5 &= 0 \\
0 &= 0
\end{aligned}
$$

Both solutions produce true statements.
The solution set for the equation is $\{-1, -5\}$

Solve each of the following quadratic equations by factoring and setting each factor equal to zero. Check by substituting answers back in the original equation.

1. $x^2 + x - 6 = 0$

2. $y^2 - 2y - 8 = 0$

3. $a^2 + 2a - 15 = 0$

4. $y^2 - 5y + 4 = 0$

5. $b^2 - 9b + 14 = 0$

6. $x^2 - 3x - 4 = 0$

7. $y^2 + y - 20 = 0$

8. $d^2 + 6d + 8 = 0$

9. $y^2 - 7y + 12 = 0$

10. $x^2 - 3x - 28 = 0$

11. $a^2 - 5a + 6 = 0$

12. $b^2 + 3b - 10 = 0$

13. $a^2 + 7a - 8 = 0$

14. $c^2 + 3x + 2 = 0$

15. $x^2 - x - 42 = 0$

16. $a^2 + a - 6 = 0$

17. $b^2 + 7b + 12 = 0$

18. $y^2 + 2y - 15 = 0$

19. $a^2 - 3a - 10 = 0$

20. $d^2 + 10d + 16 = 0$

21. $x^2 - 4x - 12 = 0$

Quadratic equations that have a whole number and a variable in the first term are solved the same way as the previous page. Factor the trinomial, and set each factor equal to zero to find the solution set.

Example 2:   Solve $2x^2 + 3x - 2 = 0$
$(2x - 1)(x + 2) = 0$
Set each factor equal to zero and solve:

$$
\begin{array}{rl}
2x - 1 & = 0 \\
+1 \quad +1 & \\
\hline
\dfrac{2x}{2} & = \dfrac{1}{2} \\
x & = \dfrac{1}{2}
\end{array}
\qquad
\begin{array}{rl}
x + 2 & = 0 \\
-2 \quad -2 & \\
\hline
x & = -2
\end{array}
$$

The solution set is $\left\{ \dfrac{1}{2}, -2 \right\}$

Solve the following quadratic equations.

22. $3y^2 + 4y - 32 = 0$

23. $5c^2 - 2c - 16 = 0$

24. $7d^2 + 18d + 8 = 0$

25. $3a^2 - 10a - 8 = 0$

26. $11x^2 - 31x - 6 = 0$

27. $5b^2 + 17b + 6 = 0$

28. $3x^2 - 11x - 20 = 0$

29. $5a^2 + 47a - 30 = 0$

30. $2c^2 - 5c - 25 = 0$

31. $2y^2 + 11y - 21 = 0$

32. $5a^2 + 23a - 42 = 0$

33. $3d^2 + 11d - 20 = 0$

34. $3x^2 - 10x + 8 = 0$

35. $7b^2 + 23b - 20 = 0$

36. $9a^2 - 58a + 24 = 0$

37. $4c^2 - 25c - 21 = 0$

38. $8d^2 + 53d + 30 = 0$

39. $4y^2 + 37a - 15 = 0$

40. $8a^2 + 37a - 15 = 0$

41. $3x^2 - 41x + 26 = 0$

42. $8b^2 + 2b - 3 = 0$

10.1   Solving the Difference of Two Squares

To solve the difference of two squares, first factor. Then set each factor equal to zero.

Example 3: $25x^2 - 36 = 0$

Step 1:   Factor the left hand side of the equation.

$25x^2 - 36 = 0$
$(5x + 6)(5x - 6) = 0$

Step 2:   Set each factor equal to zero and solve.

$$
\begin{array}{ccc}
5x + 6 & = 0 \\
\underline{\quad -6 \quad -6} \\
\dfrac{5x}{5} & = \dfrac{6}{5} \\
x & = -\dfrac{6}{5}
\end{array}
\qquad\qquad
\begin{array}{ccc}
5x - 6 & = 0 \\
\underline{\quad +6 \quad +6} \\
\dfrac{5x}{5} & = \dfrac{6}{5} \\
x & = \dfrac{6}{5}
\end{array}
$$

Check: Substitute each solution in the equation to check.

for $x = -\dfrac{6}{5}$:

$25x^2 - 36 = 0$

$25\left(-\dfrac{6}{5}\right)\left(-\dfrac{6}{5}\right) - 36 = 0 \longleftarrow$ Substitute $-\dfrac{6}{5}$ for x.

$25\left(\dfrac{36}{25}\right) - 36 = 0 \longleftarrow$ Cancel the 25's.

$36 - 36 = 0 \longleftarrow$ A true statement. $x = -\dfrac{6}{5}$ is a solution.

for $x = \dfrac{6}{5}$:

$25x^2 - 36 = 0$

$25\left(\dfrac{6}{5}\right)\left(\dfrac{6}{5}\right) - 36 = 0 \longleftarrow$ Substitute $\dfrac{6}{5}$ for x.

$25\left(\dfrac{36}{25}\right) - 36 = 0 \longleftarrow$ Cancel the 25's.

$36 - 36 = 0 \longleftarrow$ A true statement. $x = \dfrac{6}{5}$ is a solution.

The solution set is $\left\{\dfrac{-6}{5}, \dfrac{6}{5}\right\}$.

Find the solution sets for the following.

1. $25a^2 - 16 = 0$

2. $c^2 - 36 = 0$

3. $9x^2 - 64 = 0$

4. $100y^2 - 49 - 0$

5. $4b^2 - 81 = 0$

6. $d^2 - 25 = 0$

7. $9x^2 - 1 = 0$

8. $16a^2 - 9 = 0$

9. $36y^2 - 1 = 0$

10. $36y^2 - 25 = 0$

11. $d^2 - 16 = 0$

12. $64b^2 - 9 = 0$

13. $81a^2 - 4 = 0$

14. $64y^2 - 25 = 0$

15. $4c^2 - 49 = 0$

16. $x^2 - 81 = 0$

17. $49b^2 - 9 = 0$

18. $a^2 - 64 = 0$

19. $9x^2 - 1 = 0$

20. $4y^2 - 9 = 0$

21. $t^2 - 100 = 0$

22. $16k^2 - 81 = 0$

23. $81a^2 - 4 = 0$

24. $36b^2 - 16 = 0$

10.2   Solving Perfect Squares

When the square root of a constant, variable, or polynomial results in a constant, variable, or polynomial without irrational numbers, the expression is a **perfect square**. Some examples are 49, x^2, and $(x-2)^2$.

Example 4:   Solve the perfect square for x. $(x-5)^2 = 0$

Step 1:   Take the square root of both sides.
$$\sqrt{(x-5)^2} = \sqrt{0}$$
$$(x-5) = 0$$

Step 2:   Solve the equation.
$$(x-5) = 0$$
$$x - 5 + 5 = 0 + 5$$
$$x = 5$$

Example 5:   Solve the perfect square for x. $(x-5)^2 = 64$

Step 1:   Take the square root of both sides.
$$\sqrt{(x-5)^2} = \sqrt{64}$$
$$(x-5) = \pm 8$$
$$(x-5) = 8 \text{ and } (x-5) = -8$$

Step 2:   Solve the two equations.
$$\begin{array}{lll} (x-5) = 8 & \text{and} & (x-5) = -8 \\ x - 5 + 5 = 8 + 5 & \text{and} & x - 5 + 5 = -8 + 5 \\ x = 13 & \text{and} & x = -3 \end{array}$$

Solve the perfect square for x.

1. $(x-5)^2 = 0$

2. $(x+1)^2 = 0$

3. $(x+11)^2 = 0$

4. $(x-4)^2 = 0$

5. $(x-1)^2 = 0$

6. $(x+8)^2 = 0$

7. $(x+3)^2 = 4$

8. $(x-5)^2 = 16$

9. $(x-10)^2 = 100$

10. $(x+9)^2 = 9$

11. $(x-4.5)^2 = 25$

12. $(x+7)^2 = 36$

13. $(x+2)^2 = 49$

14. $(x-1)^2 = 4$

15. $(x+8.9)^2 = 49$

16. $(x-6)^2 = 81$

17. $(x-12)^2 = 121$

18. $(x+2.5)^2 = 64$

10.3 Completing the Square

"Completing the Square" is another way of factoring a quadratic equation. To complete the square, convert the equation into a perfect square.

Example 6:   Solve $x^2 - 10x + 9 = 0$ by completing the square.

Completing the square:

Step 1:   The first step is to get the constant on the other side of the equation. Subtract 9 from both sides:
$$x^2 - 10x + 9 - 9 = -9$$
$$x^2 - 10x = -9$$

Step 2:   Determine the coefficient of the x. The coefficient in this example is 10. Divide the coefficient by 2 and square the result.
$$(10 \div 2)^2 = 5^2 = 25$$

Step 3:   Add the resulting value, 25, to both sides:
$$x^2 - 10x + 25 = -9 + 25$$
$$x^2 - 10x + 25 = 16$$

Step 4:   Now factor the $x^2 - 10x + 25$ into a perfect square:
$$(x - 5)^2 = 16$$

Solving the perfect square:

Step 5:   Take the square root of both sides.
$$\sqrt{(x-5)^2} = \sqrt{16}$$
$$(x - 5) = \pm 4$$
$$(x - 5) = 4 \text{ and } (x - 5) = -4$$

Step 6:   Solve the two equations.
$$
\begin{array}{lll}
(x - 5) = 4 & \text{and} & (x - 5) = -4 \\
x - 5 + 5 = 4 + 5 & \text{and} & x - 5 + 5 = -4 + 5 \\
x = 9 & \text{and} & x = 1
\end{array}
$$

Solve for x by completing the square.

1. $x^2 + 2x - 3 = 0$

2. $x^2 - 8x + 7 = 0$

3. $x^2 + 6x - 7 = 0$

4. $x^2 - 16x - 36 = 0$

5. $x^2 - 14x + 49 = 0$

6. $x^2 - 4x = 0$

7. $x^2 + 12x + 27 = 0$

8. $x^2 + 2x - 24 = 0$

9. $x^2 + 12x - 85 = 0$

10. $x^2 - 8x + 15 = 0$

11. $x^2 - 16x + 60 = 0$

12. $x^2 - 8x - 48 = 0$

13. $x^2 + 24x + 44 = 0$

14. $x^2 + 6x + 5 = 0$

15. $x^2 - 11x + 5.25 = 0$

10.4   Using the Quadratic Formula

You may be asked on the Georgia Algebra I EOC Test in Mathematics to use the quadratic formula to solve an algebra problem known as a **quadratic equation**. The equation should be in the form $ax^2 + bx + c = 0$.

Example 7:   Using the quadratic formula, find x in the following equation: $x^2 - 8x = -7$.

Step 1:   Make sure the equation is set equal to 0.

$$x^2 - 8x + 7 = -7 + 7$$
$$x^2 - 8x + 7 = 0$$

The quadratic formula, $\dfrac{-b \pm \sqrt{b^2 - 4ac}}{2a}$, will be given to you on your formula sheet with your test.

Step 2:   In the formula, a is the number x^2 is multiplied by, b is the number x is multiplied by and c is the last term of the equation. For the equation in the example, $x^2 - 8x + 7$, $a = 1$, $b = -8$, and $c = 7$. When we look at the formula we notice a $\pm$ sign. This means that there will be two solutions to the equation, one when we use the plus sign and one when we use the minus sign. Substituting the numbers from the problem into the formula, we have:

$$\frac{8 + \sqrt{8^2 - (4)(1)(7)}}{2(1)} = 7 \qquad \text{or} \qquad \frac{8 - \sqrt{8^2 - (4)(1)(7)}}{2(1)} = 1$$

The solutions are $\{7, 1\}$

For each of the following equations, use the quadratic formula to find two solutions.

1. $x^2 + x - 6 = 0$

2. $y^2 - 2y - 8 = 0$

3. $a^2 + 2a - 15 = 0$

4. $y^2 - 5y + 4 = 0$

5. $b^2 - 9b + 14 = 0$

6. $x^2 - 3x - 4 = 0$

7. $y^2 + y - 20 = 0$

8. $d^2 + 6d + 8 = 0$

9. $y^2 - 7y + 12 = 0$

10. $x^2 - 3x - 28 = 0$

11. $a^2 - 5a + 6 = 0$

12. $b^2 + 3b - 10 = 0$

13. $a^2 + 7a - 8 = 0$

14. $c^2 + 3c + 2 = 0$

15. $x^2 - x - 42 = 0$

16. $a^2 + a - 6 = 0$

17. $b^2 + 7b + 12 = 0$

18. $y^2 + 2y - 15 = 0$

19. $a^2 - 3a - 10 = 0$

20. $d^2 + 10d + 16 = 0$

21. $x^2 - 4x - 12 = 0$

10.5   Pythagorean Theorem

Pythagoras was a Greek mathematician and philosopher who lived around 600 B.C. He started a math club among Greek aristocrats called the Pythagoreans. Pythagoras formulated the **Pythagorean Theorem** which states that in a **right triangle**, the sum of the squares of the legs of the triangle are equal to the square of the hypotenuse. Most often you will see this formula written as $a^2 + b^2 = c^2$. **This relationship is only true for right triangles.**

Example 8:   Find the length of side c.

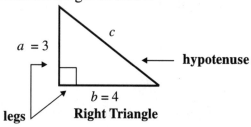

$$\text{Formula:} \quad a^2 + b^2 = c^2$$
$$3^2 + 4^2 = c^2$$
$$9 + 16 = c^2$$
$$25 = c^2$$
$$\sqrt{25} = \sqrt{c^2}$$
$$5 = c$$

Find the hypotenuse of the following triangles. Round the answers to two decimal places.

1.

$c =$ _____

2.

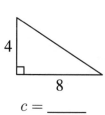

$c =$ _____

3.

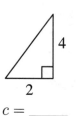

$c =$ _____

4.

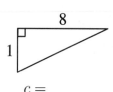

$c =$ _____

5.

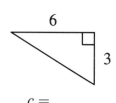

$c =$ _____

6.

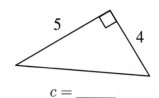

$c =$ _____

7.

$c =$ _____

8.

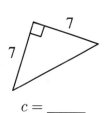

$c =$ _____

9.

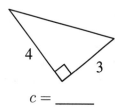

$c =$ _____

10.6   Finding the Missing Leg of a Right Triangle

In some triangles, we know the measurement of the hypotenuse as well as one of the legs. To find the measurement of the other leg, use the Pythagorean theorem by filling in the known measurements, and then solve for the unknown side.

Example 9:   Find the measure of b.

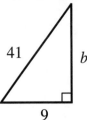

In the formula, $a^2 + b^2 = c^2$, a and b are the legs and c is always the hypotenuse.
$9^2 + b^2 = 41^2$
$81 + b^2 = 1681$
$b^2 = 1681 - 81$
$b^2 = 1600$
$\sqrt{b^2} = \sqrt{1600}$
$b = 400$

Practice finding the measure of the missing leg in each right triangle below. Simplify square roots.

1.

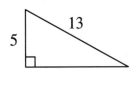

_____

4.

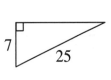

_____

7.

_____

2.

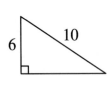

_____

5.

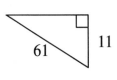

_____

8.

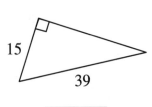

_____

3.

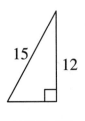

_____

6.

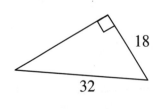

_____

9.

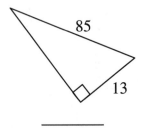

_____

Chapter 10 Review

Factor and solve each of the following quadratic equations.

1. $16b^2 - 25 = 0$

2. $a^2 - a - 30 = 0$

3. $x^2 - x = 6$

4. $100x^2 - 49 = 0$

5. $81y^2 = 9$

6. $y^2 = 21 - 4y$

7. $y^2 - 7y + 8 = 16$

8. $6x^2 + x - 2 = 0$

9. $3y^2 + y - 2 = 0$

10. $b^2 + 2b - 8 = 0$

11. $4x^2 + 19x - 5 = 0$

12. $8x^2 = 6x + 2$

13. $2y^2 - 6y - 20 = 0$

14. $-6x^2 + 7x - 2 = 0$

15. $y^2 + 3y - 18 = 0$

Using the quadratic formula, find both solutions for the variable.

16. $x^2 + 10x - 11 = 0$

17. $y^2 - 14y + 40 = 0$

18. $b^2 + 9b + 18 = 0$

19. $y^2 - 12y - 13 = 0$

20. $a^2 - 8a - 48 = 0$

21. $x^2 + 2x - 63 = 0$

22. Find the missing side.

23. Find the measure of the missing leg of the right triangle below.

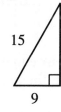

Chapter 11
Graphing and Writing Equations and Inequalities

11.1   Graphing Linear Equations

In addition to graphing ordered pairs, use the Cartesian plane to graph the solution set for an equation. Any equation with two variables that are both to the first power is called a **linear equation.** The graph of a linear equation will always be a straight line.

Example 1:   Graph the solution set for $x + y = 7$.

Step 1:   Make a list of some pairs of numbers that will work in the equation.

$$\left. \begin{array}{ll} \underline{x + y = 7} \\ 4 + 3 = 7 & (4, 3) \\ -1 + 8 = 7 & (-1, 8) \\ 5 + 2 = 7 & (5, 2) \\ 0 + 7 = 7 & 0, 7 \end{array} \right\} \text{ordered pair solutions}$$

Step 2:   Plot these points on a Cartesian plane.

Step 3:   By passing a line through these points, we graph the solution set for $x + y = 7$. This means that every point on the line is a solution to the equation $x + y = 7$. For example, $(1, 6)$ is a solution; and therefore, the line passes through the point $(1, 6)$.

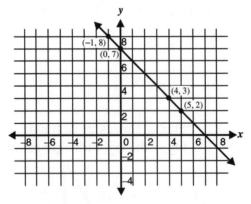

Make a table of solutions for each linear equation below. Then plot the ordered pair solutions on graph paper. Draw a line through the points. (If one of the points does not line up, you have made a mistake.)

1. $x + y = 6$

2. $y = x + 1$

3. $y = x - 2$

4. $x + 2 = y$ 5. $x - 5 = y$ 6. $x - y = 0$

Example 2:   Graph the equation $y = 2x - 5$.

Step 1:   This equation has 2 variables, both to the first power, so we know the graph will be a straight line. Substitute some numbers for x or y to find pairs of numbers that satisfy the equation. For the above equation, it will be easier to substitute values of x in order to find the corresponding value for y. Record the values for x and y in a table.

x	y
0	-5
1	-3
2	-1
3	1

If x is 0, y would be -5
If x is 1, y would be -3
If x is 2, y would be -1
If x is 3, y would be 1

Step 2:   Graph the ordered pairs, and draw a line through the points.

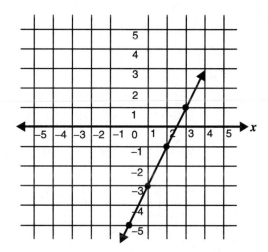

Find pairs of numbers that satisfy the equations below, and graph the line on graph paper.

1. $y = -2x + 2$ 4. $y = x + 1$ 7. $x = 4y - 3$

2. $2x - 2 = y$ 5. $4x - 2 = y$ 8. $2x = 3y + 1$

3. $-x + 3 = y$ 6. $y = 3x - 3$ 9. $x + 2y = 4$

11.2   Graphing Horizontal and Vertical Lines

The graph of some equations is a horizontal or a vertical line.

Example 3: $y = 3$

Step 1:   Make a list of ordered pairs that satisfy the equation $y = 3$.

x	y
0	3
1	3
2	3
3	3

$\left.\right\}$ No matter what value of x you choose, y is always 3.

Step 2:   Plot these points on an Cartesian plane, and draw a line through the points.

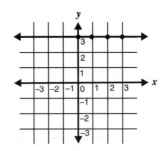

The graph is a horizontal line.

Example 4: $2x + 3 = 0$

Step 1:   For these equations with only one variable, find what x equals first.
$$2x + 3 = 0$$
$$2x = -3$$
$$x = \frac{-3}{2}$$
Just like Example 3, find ordered pairs that satisfy the equation, plot the points, and graph the line.

x	y
$\dfrac{-3}{2}$	0
$\dfrac{-3}{2}$	1
$\dfrac{-3}{2}$	2
$\dfrac{-3}{2}$	3

$\left.\right\}$ No matter which value of y you choose, the value of x does not change.

The graph is a vertical line.

Find pairs of numbers that satisfy the equations below, and graph the line on graph paper.

1. $2y + 2 = 0$

2. $x = -4$

3. $3x = 3$

4. $y = 5$

5. $4x - 2 = 0$

6. $2x - 6 = 0$

7. $4y = 1$

8. $5x + 10 = 0$

9. $3y + 12 = 0$

10. $x + 1 = 0$

11. $2y - 8 = 0$

12. $3x = -9$

13. $x = -2$

14. $6y - 2 = 0$

15. $5x - 5 = 0$

11.3   Finding the Intercepts of a Line

The is the point where the graph of a line crosses the x-axis. The is the point where the graph of a line crosses the y-axis.

To find the x-intercept, set $y = 0$

To find the y-intercept, set $x = 0$

Example 5:   Find the x- and y-intercepts of the line $6x + 2y = 18$

Step 1:   To find the x-intercept, set $y = 0$.

$$
\begin{aligned}
6x + 2(0) &= 18 \\
6x &= 18 \\
\frac{6}{6} &\quad \frac{18}{6} \\
x &= 3
\end{aligned}
$$

The x-intercept is at the point $(3, 0)$.

Step 2:   To find the x-intercept, set $x = 0$.

$$
\begin{aligned}
6(0) + 2y &= 18 \\
2y &= 18 \\
\frac{2}{2} &\quad \frac{18}{2} \\
y &= 9
\end{aligned}
$$

The y-intercept is at the point $(0, 9)$.

Step 3:   You can now use the two intercepts to graph the line.

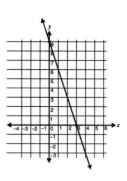

11.4   Understanding Slope

The slope of a line refers to how steep a line is. Slope is also defined as the rate of change. When we graph a line using ordered pairs, we can easily determine the slope. Slope is often represented by the letter m.

The formula for slope of a line is: $m = \dfrac{y_2 - y_1}{x_2 - x_1}$ or $\dfrac{\text{rise}}{\text{run}}$

Example 6:   What is the slope of the following line that passes through the ordered pairs $(-4, -3)$ and $(1, 3)$?

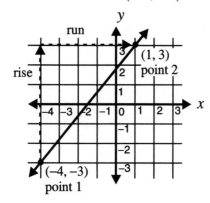

y_2 is 3, the y-coordinate of point 2.

y_1 is -3, the y-coordinate of point 1.

x_2 is 1, the x-coordinate of point 2.

x_1 is -4, the x-coordinate of point 1.

Use the formula for slope given above: $m = \dfrac{3 - (-3)}{1 - (-4)} = \dfrac{6}{5}$

The slope is $\frac{6}{5}$. This shows us that we can go up 6 (rise) and over 5 to the right (run) to find another point on the line.

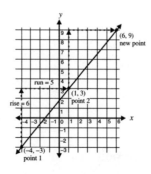

Example 7: Find the slope of a line through the points $(-2, 3)$ and $(1, -2)$. It doesn't matter which pair we choose for point 1 and point 2. The answer is the same.

Let point 1 be $(-2, 3)$
Let point 2 be $(1, -2)$

$$\text{slope} = \frac{(y_2 - y_1)}{(x_2 - x_1)} = \frac{-2 - 3}{1 - (-2)} = \frac{-5}{3}$$

When the slope is negative, the line will slant left. For this example, the line will go **down** 5 units and then over 3 units to the **right**.

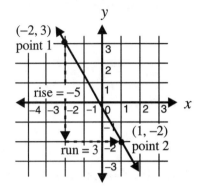

Example 8: What is the slope of a line that passes through $(1, 1)$ and $(3, 1)$?

$$\text{slope} = \frac{1 - 1}{3 - 1} = \frac{0}{2} = 0$$

When $y_2 - y_1 = 0$, the slope will equal 0, and the line will be horizontal.

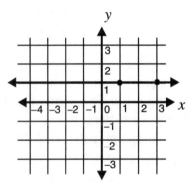

Example 9: What is the slope of a line that passes through $(2, 1)$ and $(3, 1)$?

$$\text{slope} = \frac{-3 - 1}{2 - 2} = \frac{4}{0} = \text{undefined}$$

When $x_2 - x_1 = 0$, the slope is undefined, and the line will be vertical.

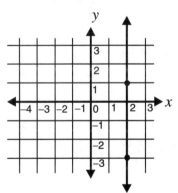

The following lines summarize what we know about slope.

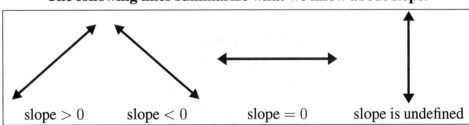

slope > 0 slope < 0 slope $= 0$ slope is undefined

Find the slope of the line that goes through the following pairs of points. Use the formula slope $= \dfrac{y_2 - y_1}{x_2 - x_1}$. Then, using graph paper, graph the line through the two points, and label the rise and run. (See Examples 6 and 7).

1. $(2, 3)$ $(4, 5)$

2. $(1, 3)$ $(2, 5)$

3. $(-1, 2)$ $(4, 1)$

4. $(1, -2)$ $(4, -2)$

5. $(3, 0)$ $(3, 4)$

6. $(3, 2)$ $(-1, 8)$

7. $(4, 3)$ $(2, 4)$

8. $(2, 2)$ $(1, 5)$

9. $(3, 4)$ $(1, 2)$

10. $(3, 2)$ $(3, 6)$

11. $(6, -2)$ $(3, -2)$

12. $(1, 2)$ $(3, 4)$

13. $(-2, 1)$ $(-4, 3)$

14. $(5, 2)$ $(4, -1)$

15. $(1, -3)$ $(-2, 4)$

16. $(2, -1)$ $(3, 5)$

11.5   Slope-Intercept Form of a Line

An equation that contains two variables, each to the first degree, is a **linear equation**. The graph for a linear equation is a straight line. To put a linear equation in slope-intercept form, solve the equation for y. This form of the equation shows the slope and the y-intercept. Slope-intercept form follows the pattern of $y = mx + b$. The "m" represents slope, and the "b" represents the y-intercept. The y-intercept is the point at which the line crosses the y-axis.

When the slope of a line is not 0, the graph of the equation shows a **direct variation** between y and x. When y increases, x increases in a certain proportion. The proportion stays constant. The constant is called the **slope** of the line.

Example 10:   Put the equation $2x + 3y = 15$ in slope-intercept form. What is the slope of the line? What is the y-intercept? Graph the line.

Step 1:   Solve for y:

$$2x + 3y = 15$$
$$-2x \qquad\qquad -2x$$
$$\frac{3y}{3} = -\frac{2x}{3} + \frac{15}{3}$$

slope-intercept form: $y = -\dfrac{2}{3}x + 5$

The slope is $-\dfrac{2}{3}$ and the y-intercept is 5.

Step 2:   Knowing the slope and the y-intercept, we can graph the line.

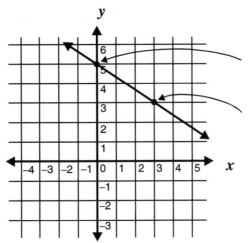

The y-intercept is 5, so the line passes through the point $(0, 5)$ on the y-axis.

The slope is $-\dfrac{2}{3}$, so go down 2 and over 3 to get a second point.

Put each of the following equations in slope-intercept form by solving for y. On your graph paper, graph the line using the slope and y-intercept.

1. $4x - 5y = 5$
2. $2x + 4y = 16$
3. $3x - 2y = 10$
4. $x + 3y = -12$
5. $6x + 2y = 0$

6. $8x - 5y = 10$
7. $-2x + y = 4$
8. $-4x + 3y = 12$
9. $-6x + 2y = 12$
10. $x - 5y = 5$

11. $3x - 2y = -6$
12. $3x + 4y = 2$
13. $-x = 2 + 4y$
14. $2x = 4y - 2$
15. $6x - 3y = 9$

16. $4x + 2y = 8$
17. $6x - y = 4$
18. $-2x - 4y = 8$
19. $5x + 4y = 16$
20. $6 = 2y - 3x$

11.6   Verify That a Point Lies On a Line

To know whether or not a point lies on a line, substitute the coordinates of the point into the formula for the line. If the point lies on the line, the equation will be true. If the point does not lie on the line, the equation will be false.

Example 11:   Does the point $(5, 2)$ line on the line given by the equation $x + y = 7$?

Solution: Substitute 5 for x and 2 for y in the equation. $5 + 2 = 7$. Since this is a true statement, the point $(5, 2)$ does line on the line $x + y = 7$.

Example 12:   Does the point $(0, 1)$ line on the line given by the equation $5x + 4y = 16$?

Solution: Substitute 0 for x and 1 for y in the equation $5x + 4y = 16$. Does $5(0) + 4(1) = 16$? No, it equals 4, not 16. Therefore, the point $(0, 1)$ is not on the line given by the equation $5x + 4y = 16$.

For each point below, state whether or not it lies on the line given by the equation that follows the point coordinates.

1. $(2,4)$ $6x - y = 8$

2. $(1,1)$ $6x - y = 5$

3. $(3,8)$ $-2x + y = 2$

4. $(9,6)$ $-2x + y = 0$

5. $(3,7)$ $x - 5y = -32$

6. $(0,5)$ $-6x - 5y = 3$

7. $(2,4)$ $4x + 2y = 16$

8. $(9,1)$ $3x - 2y = 29$

9. $(6,8)$ $6x - y = 28$

10. $(-2,3)$ $x + 2y = 4$

11. $(4,-1)$ $-x - 3y = -1$

12. $(-1,-3)$ $2x + y = 1$

11.7   Graphing a Line Knowing a Point And Slope

If you are given a point of a line and the slope of a line, you can graph the line.

Example 13:   Given that line l has a slope of $\dfrac{4}{3}$ and contains the point $(2, -1)$, graph the line.

Plot and label the point $(2, -1)$ on a Cartesian plane.

The slope, m, is $\dfrac{4}{3}$, so the rise is 4, and the run is 3. From the point $(2, -1)$, count 4 units up and 3 units to the right.

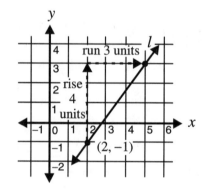

Draw the line through the two points.

Example 14:   Given a line that has a slope of $-\dfrac{1}{4}$ and passes through the point $(-3, 2)$, graph the line.

Plot the point $(-3, 2)$.

Since the slope is negative, go **down** 1 unit and over 4 units to get a second point.

Graph the line through the two points.

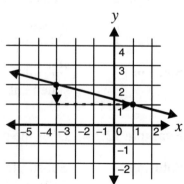

Graph a line on your own graph paper for each of the following problems. First, plot the point. Then use the slope to find a second point. Draw the line formed from the point and the slope.

1. $(2, -2)$, $m = \dfrac{3}{4}$

2. $(3, -4)$, $m = \dfrac{1}{2}$

3. $(1, 3)$, $m = -\dfrac{1}{3}$

4. $(2, -4)$, $m = 1$

5. $(3, 0)$, $m = -\dfrac{1}{2}$

6. $(-2, 1)$, $m = \dfrac{4}{3}$

7. $(-4, -2)$, $m = \dfrac{1}{2}$

8. $(1, 4)$, $m = \dfrac{3}{4}$

9. $(2, -1)$, $m = -\dfrac{1}{2}$

10. $(5, -2)$, $m = \dfrac{1}{4}$

11. $(-2, -3)$, $m = \dfrac{2}{3}$

12. $(4, -1)$, $m = -\dfrac{1}{3}$

13. $(-1, 5)$, $m = \dfrac{2}{5}$

14. $(-2, 3)$, $m = \dfrac{3}{4}$

15. $(4, 4)$, $m = -\dfrac{1}{2}$

16. $(3, -3)$, $m = -\dfrac{3}{4}$

17. $(-2, 5)$, $m = \dfrac{1}{3}$

18. $(-2, -3)$, $m = -\dfrac{3}{4}$

19. $(4, -3)$, $m = \dfrac{2}{3}$

20. $(1, 4)$, $m = -\dfrac{1}{2}$

11.8   Finding the Equation of a Line Using Two Points or a Point and Slope

If you can find the slope of a line and know the coordinates of one point, you can write the equation for the line. You know the formula for the slope of a line is:

$$m = \frac{y_2 - y_1}{x_2 - x_1} \text{ or } \frac{y_2 - y_1}{x_2 - x_1} = m$$

Using algebra, you can see that if you multiply both sides of the equation by $x_2 - x_1$, you get:

$y - y_1 = m(x - x_1) \longleftarrow$ point-slope form of an equation

Example 15:   Write the equation of the line passing through the points $(-2, 3)$ and $(1, 5)$.

Step 1:   First, find the slope of the line using the two points given.
$$m = \frac{y_2 - y_1}{x_2 - x_1} = \frac{5 - 3}{1 - (-2)} = \frac{2}{3}$$

Step 2:   Pick one of the two points to use in the point-slope equation. For point $(-2, 3)$, we know $x_1 = -2$ and $y_1 = 3$, and we know $m = \dfrac{2}{3}$. Substitute these values into the point-slope form of the equation.
$$y - y_1 = m(x - x_1)$$
$$y - 3 = \frac{2}{3}[x - (-2)]$$
$$y - 3 = \frac{2}{3}x + \frac{4}{3}$$
$$y = \frac{2}{3}x + \frac{13}{3}$$

Use the point-slope formula to write an equation for each of the following lines.

1. $(1, -2)$, $m = 2$

2. $(-3, 3)$, $m = \dfrac{1}{3}$

3. $(4, 2)$, $m = \dfrac{1}{4}$

4. $(5, 0)$, $m = 1$

5. $(3, -4)$, $m = \dfrac{1}{2}$

6. $(-1, -4)$ $(2, -1)$

7. $(2, 1)$ $(-1, -3)$

8. $(-2, 5)$ $(-4, 3)$

9. $(-4, 3)$ $(2, -1)$

10. $(3, 1)$ $(5, 5)$

11. $(-3, 1)$, $m = 2$

12. $(-1, 2)$, $m = \dfrac{4}{3}$

13. $(2, -5)$, $m = -2$

14. $(-1, 3)$, $m = \dfrac{1}{3}$

15. $(0, -2)$, $m = -\dfrac{3}{2}$

11.9   Changing the Slope or Y-Intercept of a Line

When the slope and/or the y-intercept of a linear equation changes, the graph of the line will also change.

Example 16:   Consider line l shown in Figure 1 at right. What happens to the graph of the line if the slope is changed to $\dfrac{4}{5}$?

Determine the y-intercept of the line. For line l, it can easily be seen from the graph that the y-intercept is at the point $(0, -1)$.

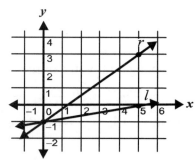

Figure 1

Find the slope of the line using two points that the line goes through: $(0, -1)$ and $(5, 0)$.

$$m = \frac{y_2 - y_1}{x_2 - x_2} = \frac{0 - (-1)}{5 - 0} = \frac{1}{5}$$

Write the equation of line l in slope-intercept form:

$$y = mx + b \implies y = \frac{1}{5}x - 1$$

Rewrite the equation of the line using a slope of $\dfrac{4}{5}$, and then graph the line. The equation of the new line is $y = \dfrac{4}{5}x - 1$.

The graph of the new line is labeled line r and is shown in Figure 1. A line with a slope of $\dfrac{4}{5}$ is steeper than a line with a slope of $\dfrac{1}{5}$.

Note: The greater the numerator, or "rise," of the slope, the steeper the line will be. The greater the denominator, or "run," of the slope, the flatter the line will be.

Example 17:   Consider line l shown in Figure 2 below. The equation of the line is $y = -\frac{1}{2}x + 3$. What happens to the graph of the line if the y-intercept is changed to -1?

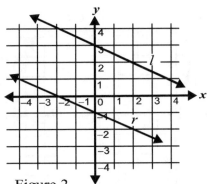

Figure 2

Rewrite the equation of the line replacing the y-intercept with -1. The equation of the new line is $y = -\frac{1}{2}x - 1$.

Graph the new line. Line r in Figure 2 is the graph of the equation $y = -\frac{1}{2}x - 1$. Since both lines l and r have the same slope, they are parallel. Line r, with a y-intercept of -1, sits below line l, with a y-intercept of 3.

Put each pair of the following equations in slope-intercept form. Write P if the lines are parallel and NP if the lines are not parallel.

1. $y = x + 1$ _____
    $2y - 2x = 6$

2. $2x + y = 6$ _____
    $2x = 8 - y$

3. $x + 5y = 0$ _____
    $5y + 5 = x$

4. $y = 3 - \frac{1}{3}x$ _____
    $3y + x = -6$

5. $x = 2y$ _____
    $-x = -2y + 14$

6. $y = x + 2$ _____
    $-y = x + 4$

7. $y = 4 - \frac{1}{4}x$ _____
    $3x + 4y = 4$

8. $x + y = 5$ _____
    $5 - y = 2x$

9. $x - 4y = 0$ _____
    $4y = x - 8$

Consider the line (l) shown on each of the following graphs, and write the equation of the line in the space provided. Then, on the same graph, graph the line (r) for which the equation is given. Write how the slope and y-intercept of line l compare to the slope and y-intercept of line r for each graph.

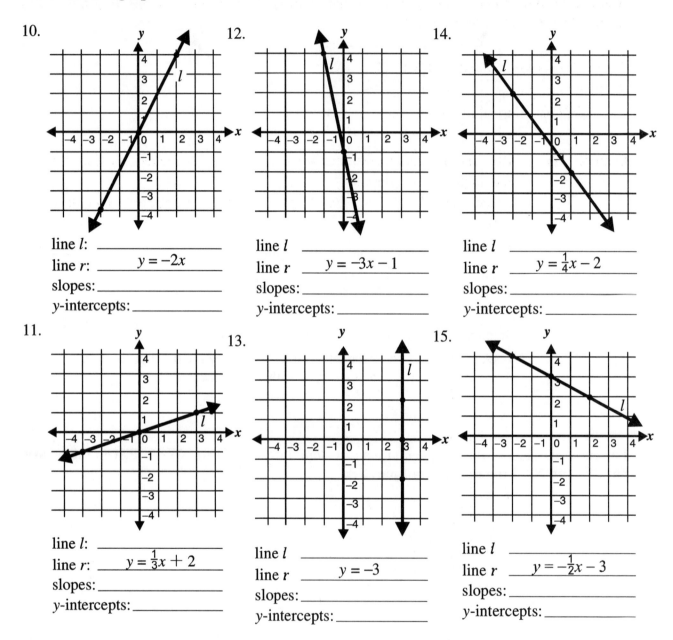

10.

line l: _____

line r: _____ $y = -2x$ _____

slopes: _____

y-intercepts: _____

12.

line l _____

line r _____ $y = -3x - 1$ _____

slopes: _____

y-intercepts: _____

14.

line l _____

line r _____ $y = \frac{1}{4}x - 2$ _____

slopes: _____

y-intercepts: _____

11.

line l: _____

line r: _____ $y = \frac{1}{3}x + 2$ _____

slopes: _____

y-intercepts: _____

13.

line l _____

line r _____ $y = -3$ _____

slopes: _____

y-intercepts: _____

15.

line l _____

line r _____ $y = -\frac{1}{2}x - 3$ _____

slopes: _____

y-intercepts: _____

11.10   Equations of Perpendicular Lines

Now that we know how to calculate the slope of lines using two points, we are going to learn how to calculate the slope of a line perpendicular to a given line, then find the equation of that perpendicular line. To find the slope of a line perpendicular to any given line, take the slope of the first line, m:

1. multiply the slope by -1

2. invert (or flip over) the slope

You now have the slope of a perpendicular line. Writing the equation for a line perpendicular to another line involves three steps:

1. find the slope of the perpendicular line

2. choose one point on the first line

3. use the point-slope form to write the equation

Example 18:   The solid line on the graph below has a slope of $\dfrac{2}{3}$. Write the equation of a line perpendicular to the solid line.
Find the slope of the perpendicular line. Multiply the slope by -1 and then flip it over.

$$\frac{2}{3} \times -1 = -\frac{2}{3} \curvearrowright -\frac{3}{2}$$

The slope of the perpendicular line, shown as a dotted line on the graph below, is $-\dfrac{3}{2}$.

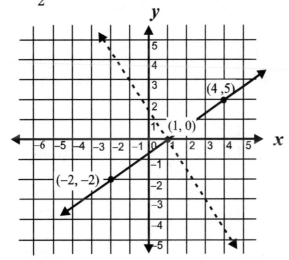

Step 2:   Choose one point on the first line. We will use $(1, 0)$ in this example. We could also use the point $(-2, -2)$ or $(4, 5)$.

Step 3:   Use the point-slope formula, $(y - y_1) = m(x - x_1)$, to write the equation of the perpendicular line. Remember, we chose $(1, 0)$ as our point. So, $(y - 0) = -\dfrac{3}{2}(x - 1)$. Simplified, $y = -\dfrac{3}{2}x + \dfrac{3}{2}$.

Solve the following problems involving perpendicular lines.

1. Find the slope of the line perpendicular to the solid line shown at right, and draw the perpendicular as a dotted line. Use one point on the solid line and the calculated slope to find the equation of the perpendicular line.

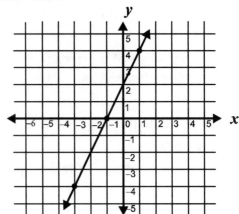

Find the equation of the perpendicular line using the point and slope given and the formula $(y - y_1) = m(x - x_1)$**.**

2. $(2, 1), 5$

3. $(3, 2), 2$

4. $(-2, 1), -3$

5. $(-4, 2), -\dfrac{1}{2}$

6. $(-1, 4), 1$

7. $(3, 3), \dfrac{2}{3}$

8. $(5, -1), -1$

9. $\left(\dfrac{1}{2}, \dfrac{3}{4}\right), 4$

10. $\left(\dfrac{2}{3}, \dfrac{3}{4}\right), -\dfrac{1}{6}$

11. $(7, -2), -\dfrac{1}{8}$

12. $(5, 0), \dfrac{4}{5}$

13. $(-3, -3), -\dfrac{7}{3}$

14. $\left(\dfrac{1}{4}, 4\right), \dfrac{1}{2}$

15. $(0, 6), -\dfrac{1}{9}$

11.11   Writing an Equation From Data

We often write data in a two-column format. If the increases or decreases in the ordered pairs are at a constant rate, then we can find a linear equation for the data.

Example 19:   Write an equation for the following set of data.

Copyright © American Book Company

Dan set his car on cruise control and noted the distance he went every 5 minutes.

Minutes in operation (x)	Odometer reading (y)
5	28,490 miles
10	28,494 miles

Step 1:   Write two order pairs in the form (minutes, distance) for Dan's driving, $(5, 28490)$ and $(10, 28494)$, and find the slope.

$$m = \frac{28494 - 28490}{10 - 5} = \frac{4}{5}$$

Step 2:   Use the ordered pairs to write the equation in the form $y = mx + b$. Place the slope, m, that you found and one of the pairs of points as x_1 and y_1 in the following formula, $y - y_1 = m(x - x_1)$.

$$y - 28490 = \frac{4}{5}(x - 5)$$
$$y - 28490 = \frac{4}{5}x - 4$$
$$y - 28490 + 28490 = \frac{4}{5}x - 4 + 28490$$
$$y + 0 = \frac{4}{5}x + 28486$$
$$y = \frac{4}{5}x + 28486$$

Write an equation for each of the following sets of data, assuming the relationship is linear.

1.

Doug's Doughnut Shop

Year in Business	Total Sales
1	$55,000
4	$85,000

3.

Jim's Depreciation on His Jet Ski

Years	Value
1	$4,500
6	$2,500

2.

Gwen's Green Beans

Days Growing	Height in Inches
2	5
6	12

4.

Stepping on the Brakes

Seconds	MPH
2	51
5	18

11.12   Graphing Linear Data

We relate many types of data by a constant ratio. As you learned on the previous page, this type of data is linear. The slope of the line described by linear data is the ratio between the data. Plotting linear data with a constant ratio can be helpful in finding additional values.

Example 20:   A department store prices socks per pair. Each pair of socks costs $0.75. Plot pairs of socks versus price on a Cartesian plane.

Step 1:   Since the price of the socks is constant, you know that one pair of socks costs $0.75, 2 pairs of socks cost $1.50, 3 pairs of socks cost $2.25, and so on. Make a list of a few points.

Pair(s) x	Price y
1	0.75
2	1.50
3	2.25

Step 2:   Plot these points on a Cartesian plane, and draw a straight line through the points.

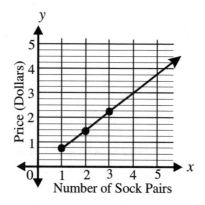

Example 21:   What is the slope of the data in the example above? What does the slope describe?

Solution: You can determine the slope either by the graph or by the data points. For this data, the slope is .75. Remember, slope is rise/run. For every $0.75 going up the y-axis, you go across one pair of socks on the x-axis. The slope describes the price per pair of socks.

Example 22:   Use the graph created in above example to answer the following questions. How much would 5 pairs of socks cost? How many pairs of socks could you purchase for $3.00? Extending the line gives useful information about the price of additional pairs of socks.

Solution 1:   The line that represents 5 pairs of socks intersects the data line at $3.75 on the y-axis. Therefore, 5 pairs of socks would cost $3.75.

Solution 2:   The line representing the value of $3.00 on the y-axis intersects the data line at 4 on the x-axis. Therefore, $3.00 will buy exactly 4 pairs of socks.

Use the information given to make a line graph for each set of data, and answer the questions related to each graph.

1. The diameter of a circle versus the circumference of a circle is a constant ratio. Use the data given below to graph a line to fit the data. Extend the line, and use the graph to answer the next question.

Circle

Diameter	Circumference
4	12.56
5	15.70

2. Using the graph of the data in question 1, estimate the circumference of a circle that has a diameter of 3 inches.

3. If the circumference of a circle is 3 inches, about how long is the diameter?

4. What is the slope of the line you graphed in question 1?

5. What does the slope of the line in question 4 describe?

6. The length of a side on a square and the perimeter of a square are constant ratios to each other. Use the data below to graph this relationship.

Square

Length of side	Perimeter
2	8
3	12

7. Using the graph from question 6, what is the perimeter of a square with a side that measure 4 inches?

8. What is the slope of the line graphed in question 6?

9. Conversions are often constant ratios. For example, converting from pounds to ounces follows a constant ratio. Use the data below to graph a line that can be used to convert pounds to ounces.

Measurement Conversion

Pounds	Ounces
2	32
4	64

10. Use the graph from question 9 to convert 40 ounces to pounds.

11. What does the slope of the line graphs for question 9 represent?

12. Graph the data below, and create a line that shows the conversion from weeks to days.

Time

Weeks	Days
1	7
2	14

13. About how many days are in $2\frac{1}{2}$ weeks?

11.13   Identifying Graphs of Linear Equations

Match each equation below with the graph of the equation.

A. $x = -4$

B. $x = y$

C. $-\frac{1}{2}x = y$

D. $y = -4$

E. $4x + y = 4$

F. $y = x - 3$

G. $x - 2y = 6$

H. $2x + 3y = 6$

I. $y = 3x + 2$

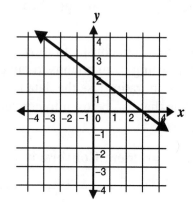

1. _____

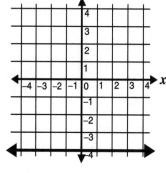

4. _____

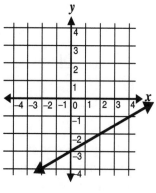

7. _____

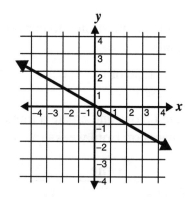

2. _____

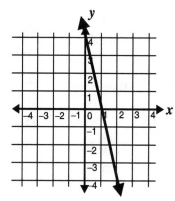

5. _____

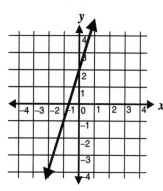

8. _____

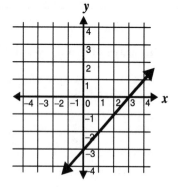

3. _____

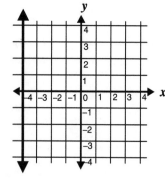

6. _____

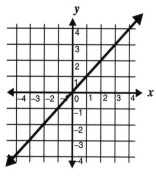

9. _____

11.14   Graphing Non-Linear Equations

Equations that you may encounter on the GA Algebra I EOCT may involve variables which are squared (raised to the second power.) The best way to find values for the x and y variables in an equation is to plug one number into x, and then find the corresponding value for y just as you did at the beginning of this chapter. Then, plot the points and draw a line through the points.

Example 23:   Graph $y = x^2$.

Step 1:   Make a table and find several values for x and y.

x	y
-2	4
-1	1
0	0
1	2
2	4

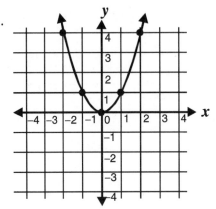

Step 2:   Plot the points, and draw a curve through the points. Notice the shape of the curve. This type of curve is called a **parabola**. Equations with one squares term will be parabolas.

Example 24:   Graph the equation $y = -2x^2 + 4$.

Step 1:   Make a table and find several values for x and y.

x	y
-2	-4
-1	2
0	4
1	2
2	-4

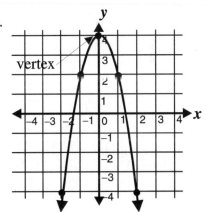

Step 2:   Plot the points, and draw a curve through the points.

Note: In the equation $y = ax^2 + c$, changing the value of a will widen or narrow the parabola around the y-axis. If the value of a is a negative number, the parabola will be reflected across the x-axis (the vertex will be at the top of the parabola instead of at the bottom.) If $a = 0$, the graph will be a straight line, not a parabola. Changing the value of c will move the vertex of the parabola from the origin to a different point on the y-axis.

Graph the equations below on a Cartesian plane.

1. $y = 2x^2$ 4. $y = -2x^2$ 7. $y = 3x^2 - 5$ 10. $y = -x^2$

2. $y = 3 - x^2$ 5. $y = x^2 + 3$ 8. $y = x^2 + 1$ 11. $y = 2x^2 - 1$

3. $y = x^2 - 2$ 6. $y = -3x^2 + 2$ 9. $y = -x^2 - 6$ 12. $y = 2 - 2x^2$

11.15   Graphing Inequalities

In the previous section, you would graph the equation $x = 3$ as:

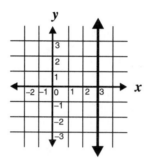

In this section, we graph inequalities such as $x > 3$ (read x is greater than 3). To show this, we use a broken line since the points on the line $x = 3$ are not included in the solution. We shade all points greater than 3.

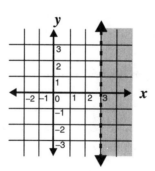

When we graph $x \geq 3$ (read x is greater than or equal to 3), we use a solid line because the points on the line $x = 3$ are included in the graph.

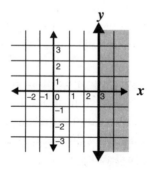

Graph the following inequalities on your own graph paper.

1. $y < 2$

2. $x \geq 4$

3. $y \geq 1$

4. $x < -1$

5. $y \geq -2$

6. $x \leq -4$

7. $x > -3$

8. $y \leq 3$

9. $x \leq 5$

10. $y > -5$

11. $x \geq 3$

12. $y < -1$

13. $x \leq 0$

14. $y > -1$

15. $y \leq 4$

16. $x \geq 0$

17. $y \geq 3$

18. $x < 4$

19. $x \leq -2$

20. $y < -2$

21. $y \geq -4$

22. $x \geq -1$

23. $y \leq 5$

24. $x < -3$

Example 25:   Graph $x + y \geq 3$.

Step 1:   First, we graph $x + y \geq 3$ by changing the inequality to an equality. Think of ordered pairs that will satisfy the equation $x + y = 3$. Then, plot the points, and draw the line. As shown below, this line divides the Cartesian plane into 2 half-planes, $x + y \geq 3$ and $x + y \leq 3$. One half-plane is above the line, and the other is below the line.

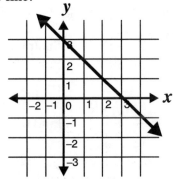

x	y
2	1
0	3
3	0
4	-1

Step 2:   To determine which side of the line to shade, first choose a test point. If the point you choose makes the inequality true, then the point is on the side you shade. If the point you choose does not make the inequality true, then shade the side that does not contain the test point.

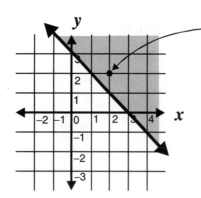

For our test point, let's choose $(2, 2)$. Substitute $(2, 2)$ into the inequality.

$$x + y \geq 3$$
$$2 + 2 \geq 3$$

$4 \geq 3$ is true, so shade the side that includes this point.

Use a solid line because of the $\geq$ sign.

Graph the following inequalities on your own graph paper.

1. $x + y \leq 4$

2. $x + y \geq 3$

3. $x \geq 5 - y$

4. $x \leq 1 + y$

5. $x - y \geq -2$

6. $x < y + 4$

7. $x + y < -1$

8. $x - y \leq 0$

9. $x \geq y + 2$

10. $x < -y + 1$

11. $-x + y > 1$

12. $-x - y < -2$

For more complex inequalities, it is easier to graph by first changing the inequality to an equality and then put the equation in slope-intercept form.

Example 26:   Graph the inequality $2x + 4y \leq 8$.

Step 1:   Change the inequality to an equality.
$2x + 4y = 8$

Step 2:   Put the equation in slope-intercept form by solving the equation for y.

$$2x + 4y = 8$$
$$2x - 2x + 4y = -2x + 8 \qquad \text{Subtract } 2x \text{ from both sides of the equation.}$$
$$4y = -2x + 8 \qquad \text{Simplify.}$$
$$\frac{4y}{4} = \frac{-2x + 8}{4} \qquad \text{Divide both sides by 4.}$$
$$y = \frac{-2x}{4} + \frac{8}{4} \qquad \text{Find the lowest terms of the fractions.}$$
$$y = -\tfrac{1}{2}x + 2$$

Step 3:   Graph the line. If the inequality is $<$ or $>$, use a dotted line. If the inequality is $\leq$ or $\geq$, use a solid line. For this example, we should use a solid line.

Step 4:   Determine which side of the line to shade. Pick a point such as $(0, 0)$ to see if it is true in the inequality.

$2x + 4y \leq 8$, so substitute $(0, 0)$.
Is $0 + 0 \leq 8$? Yes, $0 \leq 8$, so shade the side of the line that includes the point $(0, 0)$.

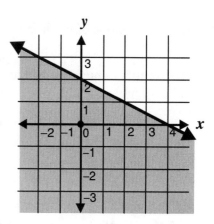

Graph the following inequalities on your own graph paper.

1. $2x + y \geq 1$

2. $3x - y \leq 3$

3. $x + 3y > 12$

4. $4x - 3y < 12$

5. $y \geq 3x + 1$

6. $x - 2y > -2$

7. $x \leq y + 4$

8. $x + y < -1$

9. $-4y \geq 2x + 1$

10. $x \leq 4y - 2$

11. $3x - y \geq 4$

12. $y \geq 2x - 5$

13. $x + 7y < 1$

14. $-2y < 4x - 1$

15. $y > 4x + 1$

Chapter 11 Review

1. Graph the solution set for the linear equation: $x - 3 = y$ on your own graph paper.

2. Which of the following is not a solution of $3x = 5y - 1$?

    (A) $(3, 2)$
    (B) $(7, 4)$
    (C) $\left(-\frac{1}{3}, 0\right)$
    (D) $(-2, -1)$

3. $(-2, 1)$ is a solution for which of the following equations?

    (A) $y + 2x = 4$
    (B) $-2x - y = 5$
    (C) $x + 2y = -4$
    (D) $2x - y = -5$

4. Graph the equation $2x - 4 = 0$ on your own graph paper.

5. What is the slope of the line that passes through the points $(5, 3)$ and $(6, 1)$?

6. What is the slope of the line that passes through the points $(-1, 4)$ and $(-6, -2)$?

7. What is the x-intercept for the following equation? $6x - y = 30$

8. What is the y-intercept for the following equation? $4x + 2y = 28$

9. Graph the equation $3y = 9$ on your own graph paper.

10. Write the following equation in slope-intercept form.
$$3x = -2y + 4$$

11. What is the slope of the line $y = -\frac{1}{2}x + 3$?

12. What is the x-intercept of the line $y = 5x + 6$?

13. What is the y-intercept of the line $y - \frac{2}{3}x + 3 = 0$?

14. Graph the line which has a slope of -2 and a y-intercept of -3 on your own graph paper.

15. Which of the following points does **not** lie on the line $y = 3x - 2$?

16. Find the equation of the line which contains the point $(0, 2)$ and has a slope of $\frac{3}{4}$.

(A) $(0, -2)$
(B) $(1, 1)$
(C) $(-1, 5)$
(D) $(2, 4)$

17. Which is the graph of $x - 3y = 6$?

(A)

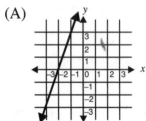

(B)

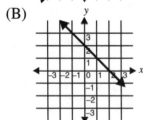

(C)

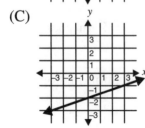

(D)

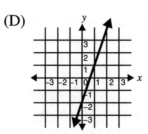

Graph the following inequalities on a Cartesian plane using your graph paper.

18. $x \geq 4$

19. $x \leq -2$

20. $5y > -10x + 5$

21. $y \leq 2$

22. $2x + y < 5$

23. $y - 2x \leq 3$

24. $y \geq x + 2$

25. $3 + y > x$

26. Paulo turns on the oven to preheat it. After one minute, the oven temperature is $200°$. After 2 minutes, the oven temperature is $325°$.

Oven Temperature

Minutes	Temperature
1	$200°$
2	$325°$

Assuming the oven temperature rises at a constant rate, write an equation that fits the data.

27. Write an equation that fits the data given below. Assume the data is linear.

Plumber Charges per Hour

Hour	Charge
1	$170
2	$220

28. What is the name of the curve described by the equation $y = 2x^2 - 1$?

29. Graph the equation $y = -\frac{1}{2}x^2 + 1$ on your own graph paper.

30. What happens to a graph if the slope changes from 2 to −2?

    (A) The graph will move down 4 spaces.
    (B) The graph will slant downward towards the left instead of the right.
    (C) The graph will flatten out to be more vertical.
    (D) The graph will slant downward towards the right instead of the left.

31. What happens to a graph is the y-intercept changes from 4 to −2?

    (A) The graph will move down 2 spaces.
    (B) The graph will slant towards the left instead of the right.
    (C) The graph will move down 6 spaces.
    (D) The graph will move up 6 spaces.

32. The graph of the line $y = 3x - 1$ is shown below. On the same graph, draw the line $y = -\frac{1}{3}x - 1$.

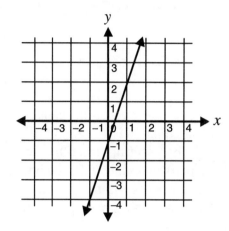

Chapter 12
Systems of Equations and Systems of Inequalities

We call two linear equations considered at the same time a **system** of linear equations. The graph of a linear equation is a straight line. The graphs of two linear equations can show that the lines are **parallel**, **intersecting**, or **collinear**. Two lines that are **parallel** will never intersect and have no ordered pairs in common. If two lines are **intersecting**, they have one point in common, and in this chapter, you will learn to find the ordered pair for that point. If the graph of two linear equations is the same line, we say the lines are **collinear**.

If you are given a system of two linear equations, and you put both equations in slope-intercept form, you can immediately tell if the graph of the lines will be **parallel**, **intersecting**, or **collinear**.

If two linear equations have the same slope and the same y-intercept, then they are both equations for the same line. They are called **collinear** or **coinciding** lines. A line is made up of an infinite number of points extending infinitely far in two directions. Therefore, collinear lines have an infinite number of points in common.

Example 1: $2x + 3y = -3$ **In slope intercept form:** $y = -\dfrac{2}{3}x - 1$

$4x + 6y = -6$ **In slope intercept form:** $y = -\dfrac{2}{3}x - 1$

The slope and y-intercept of both lines are the same.

If two linear equations have the same slope but different y-intercepts, they are **parallel** lines. Parallel lines never touch each other, so they have no points in common.

If two linear equations have different slopes, then they are intersecting lines and share exactly one point in common.

The chart below summarizes what we know about the graphs of two equations in slope-intercept form.

y-Intercepts	Slopes	Graphs	Number of Solutions
same	same	collinear	infinite
different	same	distinct parallel lines	none (they never touch)
same or different	different	intersecting lines	exactly one

For the pairs of equations below, put each equation in slope-intercept form, and tell whether the graphs of the lines will be collinear, parallel, or intersecting.

1. $x - y = -1$
   $-x + y = -1$

2. $x - 2y = 4$
   $-x + 2y = 6$

3. $y - 2 = x$
   $x + 2 = y$

4. $x = y - 1$
   $-x = y - 1$

5. $2x + 5y = 10$
   $4x + 10y = 20$

6. $x + y = 3$
   $x - y = 1$

7. $2y = 4y - 6$
   $-6x + y = 3$

8. $x + y = 5$
   $2x + 2y = 10$

9. $2x = 3y - 6$
   $4x = 6y - 6$

10. $2x - 2 = 2$
    $3y = -x + 5$

11. $x = -y$
    $x = 4 - y$

12. $2x = y$
    $x + y = 3$

13. $x = y + 1$
    $y = x + 1$

14. $x - 2y = 4$
    $-2x + 4y = -8$

15. $2x + 3y = 4$
    $-2x + 3y = -8$

16. $2x - 4y = 1$
    $-6x + 12y = 3$

17. $-3x + 4y = 1$
    $6x + 8y = 2$

18. $x + y = 2$
    $5x + 5y = 10$

19. $x + y = 4$
    $x - y = 4$

20. $y = -x + 3$
    $x - y = 1$

12.1   Finding Common Solutions for Intersecting Lines

When two lines intersect, they share exactly one point in common.

Example 2: $3x + 4y = 20$ and $4x + 2y = 12$

Put each equation in slope-intercept form.

$$3x + 4y = 20 \qquad\qquad 2y - 4x = 12$$
$$4y = -3x + 20 \qquad\qquad 2y = 4x + 12$$
$$y = -\tfrac{3}{4}x + 5 \qquad\qquad y = 2x + 6$$

slope-intercept form

Straight lines with different slopes are **intersecting lines**. Look at the graphs of the lines on the same Cartesian plane.

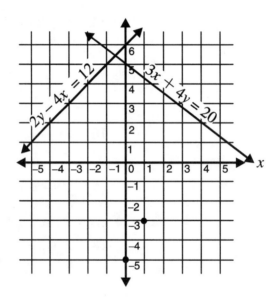

You can see from looking at the graph that the intersecting lines share one point in common. However, it is hard to tell from looking at the graph what the coordinates are for the point of intersection. To find the exact point of intersection, you can use the **substitution method** to solve the system of equations algebraically.

12.2   Solving Systems of Equations by Substitution

You can solve systems of equations by using the substitution method.

Example 3:   Find the point of intersection of the following two equations:

Equation 1: $x - y = 3$

Equation 2: $2x + y = 9$

Step 1: Solve one of the equations for x or y. Let's choose to solve equation 1 for x.

Equation 1: $\qquad x - y = 3$

$$x = y + 3$$

Step 2: Substitute the value of x from equation 1 in place of x in equation 2.

Equation 2: $\qquad 2x + y = 9$
$$2(y + 3) + y = 9$$
$$2y + 6 + y = 9$$
$$3y + 6 = 9$$
$$3y = 3$$
$$y = 1$$

Step 3: Substitute the solution for y back in equation 1 and solve for x.

Equation 1: $\qquad x - y = 3$
$$x - 1 = 3$$
$$x = 4$$

Step 4: The solution set is $(4, 1)$. Substitute in one or both of the equations to check.

Equation 1: $\qquad x - y = 3 \qquad$ Equation 2: $\qquad 2x + 9 = 9$

$\qquad\qquad\qquad 4 - 1 = 3 \qquad\qquad\qquad\qquad\quad 2(4) + 1 = 9$

$\qquad\qquad\qquad 3 = 3 \qquad\qquad\qquad\qquad\qquad\quad 8 + 1 = 9$

$\qquad\qquad\qquad\qquad\qquad\qquad\qquad\qquad\qquad\qquad\quad 9 = 9$

The point $(4, 1)$ is common for both equations. This is the **point of intersection**.

For each of the following pairs of equations, find the point of intersection, the common solution, using the substitution method.

1. $x + 2y = 8$
   $2x - 3y = 2$

2. $x - y = -5$
   $x + y = 1$

3. $x - y = 4$
   $x + y = 2$

4. $x - y = -1$
   $x + y = 9$

5. $-x + y = 2$
   $x + y = 8$

6. $x + 4y = 10$
   $x + 5y = 10$

7. $2x + 3y = 2$
   $4x - 9y = -1$

8. $x + 3y = 5$
   $x - y = 1$

9. $-x = y - 1$
   $x = y - 1$

10. $x - 2y = 2$
      $2y + x = -2$

12. $3x - y = 2$
      $5x + y = 6$

14. $x - y = 1$
      $-x - y = 1$

11. $5x + 2y = 1$
      $2x + 4y = 10$

13. $2x + 3y = 3$
      $4x + 5y = 5$

15. $x = y + 3$
      $y = 3 - x$

12.3   Solving Systems of Equations by Adding or Subtracting

You can solve systems of equations algebraically by adding or subtracting an equation from another equation or system of equations.

Example 4:   Find the point of intersection of the following two equations:
Equation 1: $x + y = 10$
Equation 2: $-x + 4y = 5$

Step 1:   Eliminate one of the variables by adding the two equations together. Since the x has the same coefficient in each equation, but opposite signs, it will cancel nicely by adding.

$$\begin{array}{r} x + y = 10 \\ +\,(-x + 4y = 5) \\ \hline 0 + 5y = 15 \\ 5y = 15 \\ y = \ 3 \end{array}$$ Add each like term together.
Simplify.
Divide both sides by 5.

Step 2:   Substitute the solution for y back into an equation, and solve for x.
Equation 1: $x + y = 10$ Substitute 3 for y.
$x + 3 = 10$ Subtract 3 from both sides.
$x = \ 7$

Step 3:   The solution set is $(7, 3)$. To check, substitute the solution into both of the original equations.

Equation 1: $x + y = 10$ Equation 2: $-x + 4y = 5$
$7 + 3 = 10$ $-(7) + 4(3) = 5$
$10 = 10$ $-7 + 12 = 5$
$5 = 5$

The point $(7, 3)$ is the point of intersection.

Example 5:   Find the point of intersection of the following two equations:
Equation 1: $3x - 2y = -1$
Equation 2: $-4y = -x - 7$

Step 1:   Put the variables on the same side of each equation. Take equation 2 out of y-intercept form.
$-4y = -x - 7$ Add x to both sides.
$x - 4y = -x + x - 7$ Simplify.
$x - 4y = -7$

Step 2:   Add the two equations together to cancel one variable. Since each variable has the same sign and different coefficients, we have to multiply one equation by a

150   Copyright © American Book Company

negative number so one of the variables will cancel. Equation 1's y variable has a coefficient of 2, and if multiplied by -2, the y will have the same variable as the y in equation 2, but a different sign. This will cancel nicely when added.

$$-2\left(3x - 2y = -1\right) \qquad \text{Multiply by } -2.$$
$$-6x + 4y = 2$$

Step 3:   Add the two equations.

$$
\begin{array}{ll}
-6x + 4y = 2 & \\
\underline{+\left(x - 4y = -7\right)} & \text{Add equation 2 to equation 1.} \\
-5x + 0 = -5 & \text{Simplify.} \\
\quad -5x = -5 & \text{Divide both sides by } -5. \\
\qquad x = 1 &
\end{array}
$$

Step 4:   Substitute the solution for x back into an equation and solve for y.

$$
\begin{array}{lll}
\text{Equation 1:} & 3x - 2y = -1 & \text{Substitute 1 for } x. \\
& 3\left(1\right) - 2y = -1 & \text{Simplify.} \\
& 3 - 2y = -1 & \text{Subtract 3 from both sides.} \\
& 3 - 3 - 2y = -1 - 3 & \text{Simplify.} \\
& -2y = -4 & \text{Divide both sides by } -2. \\
& y = 2 &
\end{array}
$$

Step 5:   The solution set is $(1, 2)$. To check, substitute the solution into both of the original equations.

$$
\begin{array}{llll}
\text{Equation 1:} & 3x - 2y = -1 & \quad \text{Equation 2:} & -4y = -x - 7 \\
& 3\left(1\right) - 2\left(2\right) = -1 & & -4\left(2\right) = -1 - 7 \\
& 3 - 4 = -1 & & -8 = -8 \\
& -1 = -1 & &
\end{array}
$$

The point $(1, 2)$ is the point of intersection.

For each of the following pairs of equations, find the point of intersection by adding the two equations together. Remember you might need to change the coefficients and/or signs of the variables before adding.

1. $x + 2y = 8$
    $-x - 3y = 2$

2. $x - y = 5$
    $2x + y = 1$

3. $x - y = -1$
    $x + y = 9$

4. $3x - y = -1$
    $x + y = 13$

5. $-x + 4y = 2$
    $x + y = 8$

6. $x + 4y = 10$
    $x + 7y = 16$

7. $2x - y = 2$
    $4x - 9y = -3$

8. $x + 3y = 13$
    $5x - y = 1$

9. $-x = y - 1$
    $x = y - 1$

10. $x - y = 2$
     $2y + x = 5$

11. $5x + 2y = 1$
     $4x + 8y = 20$

12. $3x - 2y = 14$
     $x - y = 6$

13. $2x + 3y = 3$
     $3x + 5y = 5$

14. $x - 4y = 6$
     $-x - y = -1$

15. $x = 2y + 3$
     $y = 3 - x$

12.4   Graphing Systems of Inequalities

We solve systems of inequalities best graphically. Look at the following example.

Example 6:   Sketch the solution set of the following system of inequalities:

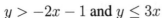

$$y > -2x - 1 \text{ and } y \leq 3x$$

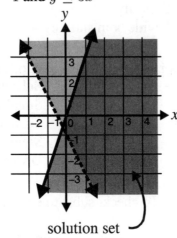

solution set

Step 1:   Graph both inequalities on a Cartesian plane. Study the chapter on graphing inequalities if you need to review.

Step 2:   Shade the portion of the graph that represents the solution set to each inequality just as you did in the chapter on graphing inequalities.

Step 3:   Any shaded region that overlaps is the solution set of both inequalities.

Graph the following systems of inequalities on your own graph paper. Shade and identify the solution set for both inequalities.

1. $2x + 2y \geq -4$
    $3y < 2x + 6$

2. $7x + 7y \leq 21$
    $8x < 6y - 24$

3. $9x + 12y < 36$
    $34x - 17y > 34$

4. $-11x - 22y \geq 44$
    $-4x + 2y \leq 8$

5. $24x < 72 + 36y$
    $11x + 22y \leq -33$

6. $15x - 60 < 30y$
    $20x + 10y < 40$

7. $-12x + 24y > -24$
    $10x < -5y + 15$

8. $y \geq 2x + 2$
    $y < -x - 3$

9. $3x + 4y \geq 12$
    $y > -3x + 2$

10. $-3x \leq 6 + 2y$
    $y \geq -x - 2$

11. $2x - 2y \leq 4$
    $3x + 3y \leq -9$

12. $-x \geq -2y - 2$
    $-2x - 2y > 4$

Chapter 12 Review

For each pair of equations below, tell whether the graphs of the lines will be collinear, parallel, or intersecting.

1. $y = 4x + 1$
   $y = 4x - 3$

2. $y - 4 = x$
   $2x + 8 = 2y$

3. $x + y = 5$
   $x - y = -1$

4. $2y - 3x = 6$
   $4y = 6x + 8$

5. $5y = 3x - 7$
   $4x - 3y = -7$

6. $2x - 2y = 2$
   $y - x = -1$

Find the common solution for each of the following pairs of equations, using the substitution method.

7. $x - y = 2$
   $x + 4y = -3$

8. $x + y = 1$
   $x + 3y = 1$

9. $-4y = -2x + 4$
   $-x = -2y - 2$

10. $2x + 8y = 20$
    $5y = 12 - x$

11. $x = y - 3$
    $-x = y + 3$

12. $-2x + y = -3$
    $x - y = 9$

Graph the following systems of inequalities on your own graph paper. Identify the solution set to both inequalities.

13. $x + 2y \geq 2$
    $2x - y \leq 4$

14. $20x + 10y \leq 40$
    $3x + 2y \geq 6$

15. $6x + 8y \leq -24$
    $-4x + 8y \geq 16$

16. $14x - 7y \geq -28$
    $3x + 4y \leq -12$

17. $2y \geq 6x + 6$
    $2x - 4y \geq -4$

18. $9x - 6y \geq 18$
    $3y \geq 6x - 12$

Find the point of intersection for each pair of equations by adding and/or subtracting the two equations.

19. $2x + y = 4$
    $3x - y = 6$

20. $x + 2y = 3$
    $x + 5y = 0$

21. $x + y = 1$
    $y = x + 7$

22. $2x + 4y = 5$
    $3x + 8y = 9$

23. $2x - 2y = 7$
    $3x - 5y = \frac{5}{2}$

24. $x - 3y = -2$
    $y = -\frac{1}{3}x + 4$

Chapter 13
Relations and Functions

13.1 Relations

A **relation** is a set of ordered pairs. We call the set of the first members of each ordered pair the **domain** of the relation. We call the set of the second members of each ordered pairs the **range**.

Example 1: State the domain and range of the following relation:
$$\{(2,4), (3,7), (4,9), (6,11)\}$$
Solution: Domain: $\{2,3,4,6\}$ the first member of each ordered pair
Range: $\{4,7,9,11\}$ the second member of each ordered pair

State the domain and range for each relation.

1. $\{(2,5), (9,12), (3,8), (6,7)\}$

2. $\{(12,4), (3,4), (7,12), (26,19)\}$

3. $\{(4,3), (7,14), (16,34), (5,11)\}$

4. $\{(2,45), (33,43), (98,9), (43,61), (67,54)\}$

5. $\{(78,14), (29,67), (84,49), (16,18), (98,46)\}$

6. $\{(-8,16), (23,-7), (-4,-9), (16,-8), (-3,6)\}$

7. $\{(-7,-4), (-3,16), (-4,17), (-6,-8), (-8,12)\}$

8. $\{(-1,-2), (3,6), (-7,14), (-2,8), (-6,2)\}$

9. $\{(0,9), (-8,5), (3,12), (-8,-3), (7,18)\}$

10. $\{(58,14), (44,97), (74,32), (6,18), (63,44)\}$

11. $\{(-7,0), (-8,10), (-3,11), (-7,-32), (-2,57)\}$

12. $\{(18,34), (22,64), (94,36), (11,18), (91,45)\}$

When given an equation in two variables, the domain is the set of x values that satisfies the equation. The range is the set of y values that satisfies the equation.

Example 2: Find the range of the relation $3x = y + 2$ for the domain $\{-1,0,1,2,3\}$.
Solve the equation for each value of x given. The result, the y values, will be the range.

	Given:			**Solution:**	

x	y
-1	
0	
1	
2	
3	

x	y
-1	-5
0	-2
1	1
2	4
3	7

The range is $\{-5, -2, 1, 4, 7\}$.

Find the range of each relation for the given domain.

	Relation	**Domain**	**Range**
1.	$y = 5x$	$\{1, 2, 3, 4\}$	
2.	$y = |x|$	$\{-3, -2, -1, 0, 1\}$	
3.	$y = 3x + 2$	$\{0, 1, 3, 4\}$	
4.	$y = -|x|$	$\{-2 - 1, 0, 1, 2\}$	
5.	$y = -2x + 1$	$\{0, 1, 3, 4\}$	
6.	$y = 10x - 2$	$\{-2 - 1, 0, 1, 2\}$	
7.	$y = 3|x| + 1$	$\{-2 - 1, 0, 1, 2\}$	
8.	$y - x = 0$	$\{1, 2, 3, 4\}$	
9.	$y - 2x = 0$	$\{1, 2, 3, 4\}$	
10.	$y = 3x - 1$	$\{0, 1, 3, 4\}$	
11.	$y = 4x + 2$	$\{0, 1, 3, 4\}$	
12.	$y = 2|x| - 1$	$\{-2 - 1, 0, 1, 2\}$	

13.2   Determining Domain and Range From Graphs

The domain is all of the x values that lie on the function in the graph from the lowest x value to the highest x value. The range is all of the y values that lie on the function in the graph from the lowest y to the highest y.

Example 3:   Find the domain and range of the graph.

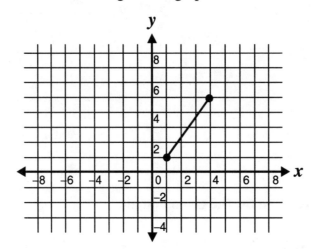

Step 1:   First find the lowest x value depicted on the graph. In this case it is 1. Then find the highest x value depicted on the graph. The highest value of x on the graph is 4. The domain must contain all of the values between the lowest x value and the highest x value. The easiest way to write this is $1 \leq$ Domain ≤ 4 or $1 \leq x \leq 4$.

Step 2:   Perform the same process for the range, but this time look at the lowest and highest y values. The answer is $1 \leq$ Range ≤ 5 or $1 \leq y \leq 5$.

Find the domain and range of each graph below. Write your answers in the line provided.

1.

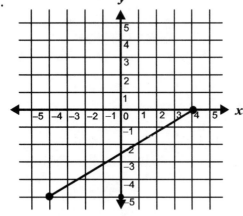

_____

2.

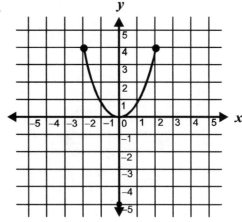

_____

3.

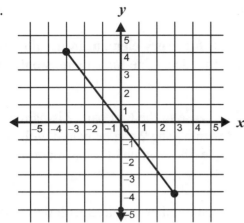

_____

4.

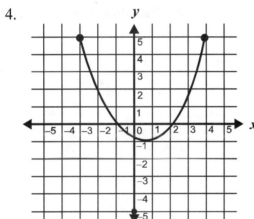

_____

5.

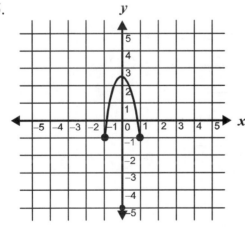

_____

6.

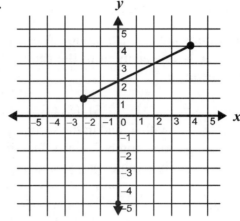

_____

7.

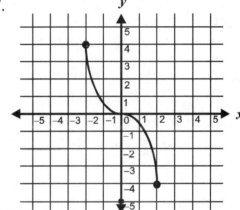

_____

8.

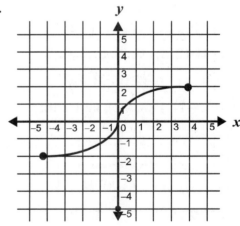

_____

13.3   Functions

Some relations are also **functions**. A relation is a function if **for every element in the domain, there is exactly one element in the range**. In other words, for each value for x there is only one unique value for y.

Example 4: $\{(2,4),(2,5),(3,4)\}$ is **NOT** a function because in the first pair, 2 is paired with 4, and in the second pair, 2 is paired with 5. The 2 can be paired with only one number to be a function. In this example, the x value of 2 has more than one value for y: 4 and 5.

Example 5: $\{(1,2),(3,2),(5,6)\}$ **IS** a function. Each first number is paired with only one second number. The 2 is repeated as a second number, but the relation remains a function.

Determine whether the ordered pairs of numbers below represent a function. Write "F" if it is a function. Write "NF" if it is not a function.

1. $\{(-1,1),(-3,3),(0,0),(2,2)\}$ _____

2. $\{(-4,-3),(-2,-3),(-1,-3),(2,-3)\}$ _____

3. $\{(5,-1),(2,0),(2,2),(5,3)\}$ _____

4. $\{(-3,3),(0,2),(1,1),(2,0)\}$ _____

5. $\{(-2,-5),(-2,-1),(-2,1),(-2,3)\}$ _____

6. $\{(0,2),(1,1),(2,2),(4,3)\}$ _____

7. $\{(4,2),(3,3),(2,2),(0,3)\}$ _____

8. $\{(-1,-1),(-2,-2),(3,-1),(3,2)\}$ _____

9. $\{(2,-2),(0,-2),(-2,0),(1,-3)\}$ _____

10. $\{(2,1),(3,2),(4,3),(5,-1)\}$ _____

11. $\{(-1,0),(2,1),(2,4),(-2,2)\}$ _____

12. $\{(1,4),(2,3),(0,2),(0,4)\}$ _____

13. $\{(0,0),(1,0),(2,0),(3,0)\}$ _____

14. $\{(-5,-1),(-3,-2),(-4,-9),(-7,-3)\}$ _____

15. $\{(8,-3),(-4,4),(8,0),(6,2)\}$ _____

16. $\{(7,-1),(4,3),(8,2),(2,8)\}$ _____

17. $\{(4,-3),(2,0),(5,3),(4,1)\}$ _____

18. $\{(2,-6),(7,3),(-3,4),(2,-3)\}$ _____

19. $\{(1,1),(3,-2),(4,16),(1,-5)\}$ _____

20. $\{(5,7),(3,8),(5,3),(6,9)\}$ _____

13.4   Recognizing Functions

Recall that a relation is a function with only one y value for every x value. We can depict functions in many ways including through graphs.

Example 6:

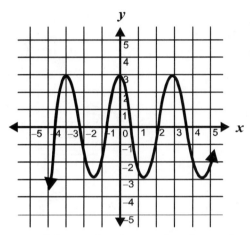

This graph **IS** a function because it has only one y value for each value of x.

Example 7:

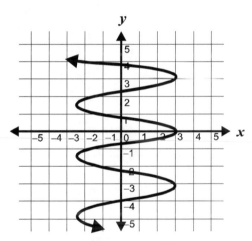

This graph is **NOT** a function because there is more than one y value for each value of x.

HINT: An easy way to determine a function from a graph is to do a vertical line test. First, draw a vertical line that crosses over the whole graph. If the line crosses the graph more than one time, then it is not a function. If it only crosses it once, it is a function. Take Example 2 above:

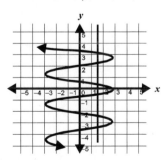

Since the vertical line passes over the graph six times, it is not a function.

Determine whether or not each of the following graphs is a function. If it is, write function on the line provided. If it is not a function, write NOT a function on the line provided.

1.

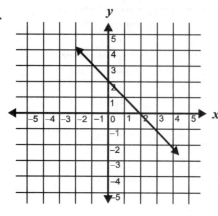

_____

4.

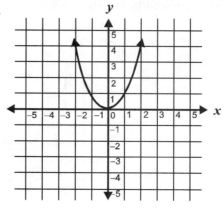

_____

2.

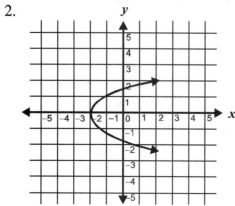

_____

5.

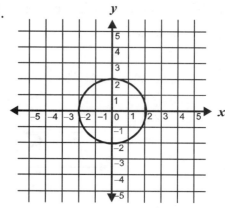

_____

3.

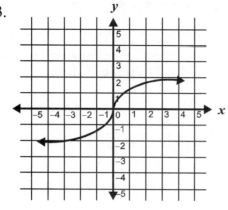

_____

6.

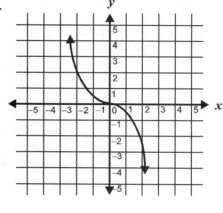

_____

7.

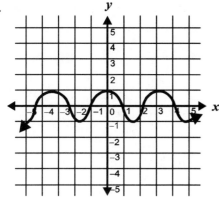

_____

10.

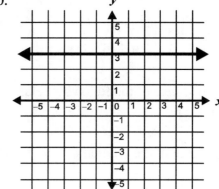

_____

8.

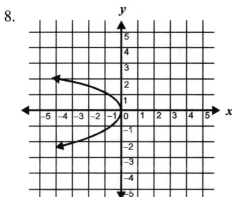

_____

11.

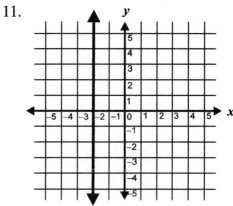

_____

9.

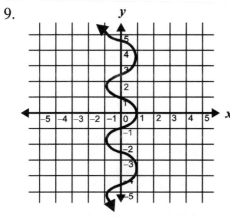

_____

12.

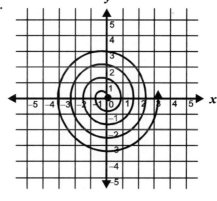

_____

161

Chapter 13 Review

1. What is the domain of the following relation?
   $\{(-1, 2), (2, 5), (4, 9), (6, 11)\}$

2. What is the range of the following relation?
   $\{(0, -2), (-1, -4), (-2, 6), (-3, -8)\}$

3. Find the range of the relation $y = 5x$ for the domain $\{0, 1, 2, 3, 4\}$.

4. Find the range of the relation $y = \dfrac{3(x-2)}{5}$ for the domain $\{-8, -3, 7, 12, 17\}$.

5. Find the range of the relation $y = 10 - 2x$ for the domain $\{-8, -4, 0, 4, 8\}$.

For each of the following relations given in questions 6–10, write F if it is a function and NF if it is not a function.

6. $\{(1, 2), (2, 2), (3, 2)\}$

7. $\{(-1, 0), (0, 1), (1, 2), (2, 3)\}$

8. $\{(2, 1), (2, 2), (2, 3)\}$

9. $\{(1, 7), (2, 5), (3, 6), (2, 4)\}$

10. $\{(0, -1), (-1, -2), (-2, -3), (-3, -4)\}$

Chapter 14
Statistics

Statistics is a branch of mathematics. Using statistics, mathematicians organize data (numbers) into forms that are easily understood.

14.1   Range

In **statistics**, the difference between the largest number and the smallest number in a list is called the **range**.

Example 1:   Find the range of the following list of numbers: 16, 73, 26, 15, and 35.

The largest number is 73, and the smallest number is 15. $73 - 15 = 58$
The range is 58.

Find the range for each list of numbers below.

1.	2.	3.	4.	5.	6.	7.
21	6	89	41	23	2	77
51	7	22	3	20	38	94
48	31	65	56	64	29	27
42	55	36	41	38	33	46
12	8	20	19	21	59	63

8.	9.	10.	11.	12.	13.	14.
51	65	84	84	21	45	62
62	54	59	65	78	57	39
32	56	48	32	6	57	96
16	5	21	50	97	14	45
59	63	80	71	45	61	14

15. 2, 15, 3, 25, and 17

16. 15, 48, 52, 41, and 8

17. 54, 74, 2, 86, and 75

18. 15, 61, 11, 22, and 65

19. 33, 18, 65, 12, and 74

20. 47, 12, 33, 25, and 19

21. 56, 10, 33, 7, 16, and 5

22. 46, 25, 78, 49, and 6

23. 45, 75, 63, and 21

24. 97, 23, 56, 12, and 66

25. 87, 44, 63, and 12

26. 84, 55, 66, 38, and 31

27. 35, 44, 81, 99, and 78

28. 95, 54, 62, 14, 8, and 3

14.2   Mean

In statistics, the mean is the same as the average. To find the mean of a list of numbers, first add together all of the numbers in the list, and then divide by the number of items in the list.

Example 2:   Find the mean of 38, 72, 110, 548.

   Step 1:   First add: $38 + 72 + 110 + 548 = 768$

   Step 2:   There are 4 numbers in the list so dive the total by 4. $768 \div 4 = 192$
   The mean is 192.

Practice finding the mean (average). Round to the nearest tenth if necessary.

1. Dinners served:
    489 561 522 450

2. Prices paid for shirts:
    $4.89 $9.97 $5.90 $8.64

3. Piglets born:
    23 19 15 21 22

4. Student absences:
    6 5 13 8 9 12 7

5. Paychecks:
    $89.56 $99.99 $56.54

6. Choir attendance:
    56 45 97 66 70

7. Long distance calls:
    33 14 24 21 19

8. Train boxcars:
    56 55 48 61 51

9. Cookies eaten:
    5 6 8 9 2 4 3

Find the mean (average) of the following word problems.

10. Val's science grades are 95, 87, 65, 94, 78, and 97. What is her average?

11. Ann runs a business from her home. The number of orders for the last 7 business days were 17, 24, 13, 8, 11, 15, and 9. What is the average number of orders per day?

12. Melissa tracks the number of phone calls she has per day: 8, 2, 5, 4, 7, 3, 6, 1. What is the average number of calls she receives?

13. The Cheese Shop tracks the number of lunches they serve this week: 42, 55, 36, 41, 38, 33, and 46. What is the average number of lunches served?

14. Leah drives 364 miles in 7 hours. What is her average miles per hour?

15. Tim saves $680 in 8 months. How much do his savings average each month?

16. Ken makes 117 passes in 13 games. How many passes does he average per game?

14.3   Finding Data Missing From the Mean

Example 3:   Mara knows she has an 88 average in her biology class, but she lost one of her papers. The three papers she could find have scores of 98%, 84%, and 90%. What is the score on her fourth paper?

Step 1:   Figure the total score on four papers with an 88% average. $.88 \times 4 = 3.52$

Step 2:   Add together the scores from the three papers you have. $.98 + .84 + .9 = 2.72$

Step 3:   Subtract the scores you know from the total score. $3.52 - 2.72 = .80$ She had 80% on her fourth paper.

Find the data missing from the following problems.

1. Gabriel earns 87% on his first geography test. He wants to keep a 92% average. What does he need to get on his next test to bring his average up?

2. Rian earns $68.00 on Monday. How much money must she earn on Tuesday to have an average of $80 earned for the two days?

3. Haley, Chuck, Dana, and Chris enter a contest to see who could bake the most chocolate chip cookies in an hour. They bake an average of 75 cookies. Haley bakes 55, Chuck bakes 70, and Dana bakes 90. How many does Chris bake?

4. Four wrestlers makes a pact to lose some weight before the competition. They lose an average of 7 pounds each over the course of 3 weeks. Carlos loses 6 pounds, Steve loses 5 pounds, and Greg loses 9 pounds. How many pounds does Wes lose?

5. Three boxes are ready for shipment. The boxes average 26 pounds each. The first box weighs 30 pounds; the second box weighs 25 pounds. How much does the third box weigh?

6. The five jockeys running in the next race average 92 pounds each. Nicole weighs 89 pounds. Jon weighs 95 pounds. Jenny and Kasey weigh 90 pounds each. How much does Jordan weigh?

7. Jessica makes three loaves of bread that weigh a total of 45 ounces. What is the average weight of each loaf?

8. Celeste makes scented candles to give away to friends. She has 2 pounds of candle wax which she melts, scents, and pours into 8 molds. What is the average weight of each candle?

9. Each basketball player has to average a minimum of 5 points a game for the next three games to stay on the team. Ben is feeling the pressure. He scores 3 points the first game and 2 points the second game. How many points does he need to score in the third game to stay on the team?

14.4   Median

In a list of numbers ordered from lowest to highest, the **median** is the middle number. To find the **median**, first arrange the numbers in numerical order. If there is an odd number of items in the list, the **median** is the middle number. If there is an even number of items in the list, the **median** is the **average of the two middle numbers.**

Example 4:   Find the median of 42, 35, 45, 37, and 41.

    Step 1:   Arrange the numbers in numerical order: 35 37 41 42 45

    Step 2:   Find the middle number. The median is 41.

Example 5:   Find the median of 14, 53, 42, 6, 14, and 46.

    Step 1:   Arrange the numbers in numerical order: 6 14 14 42 46 53.

    Step 2:   Find the average of the two middle numbers. $(14 + 42) \div 2 = 28$. The median is 28.

Circle the median in each list of numbers.

1. 35, 55, 40, 30, and 45   4. 15, 16, 19, 25, 20   7. 401, 758, and 254

2. 7, 2, 3, 6, 5, 1, and 8   5. 75, 98, 87, 65, 82, 88, 100   8. 41, 13, 14, 21, and 19

3. 65, 42, 60, 46, and 90   6. 33, 42, 50, 22, and 19   9. 5, 8, 10, 13, 1, and 8

10.	11.	12.	13.	14.	15.	16.
19	9	45	52	20	8	15
14	3	32	54	21	17	40
12	10	66	19	25	13	42
15	17	55	63	18	14	32
18	6	61	20	16	22	28

Find the median in each list of numbers.

17. 10, 8, 21, 14, 9, and 12   19. 5, 24, 9, 18, 12, and 3   21. 23, 21, 36, and 27

18. 43, 36, 20, and 40   20. 48, 13, 54, 82, 90, and 7   22. 9, 4, 3, 1, 6, 2, 10, and 12

23.	24.	25.	26.	27.	28.	29.
2	11	13	75	48	22	17
10	22	15	62	45	19	30
6	25	9	60	52	15	31
18	28	35	52	30	43	18
20	10	29	80	35	34	14
23	23	33	50	58	28	25

14.5   Mode

In statistics, the mode is the number that occurs most frequently in a list of numbers.

Example 6:   Exam grades for a Math class were as follows:
70 88 92 85 99 85 70 85 99 100 88 70 99 88 88 99 88 92 85 88.

Step 1:   Count the number of times each number occurs in the list.

70 - 3 times
88 - 6 times
92 - 2 times
85 - 4 times
99 - 4 times
100 - 1 times

Step 2:   Find the number that occurs most often.
The mode is 88 because it is listed 6 times. No other number is listed as often.

Find the mode in each of the following lists of numbers.

1.	88	2.	54	3.	21	4.	56	5.	64	6.	5	7.	12
	15		42		16		67		22		4		41
	88		44		15		67		22		9		45
	17		56		78		19		15		8		32
	18		44		21		56		14		4		16
	88		44		16		67		14		7		12
	17		56		21		20		22		4		12

8. 48, 32, 56, 32, 56, 48, 56

9. 12, 16, 54, 78, 16, 25, 20

10. 5, 4, 8, 3, 4, 2, 7, 8, 4, 2

11. 11, 9, 7, 11, 7, 5, 7, 7, 5

12. 84, 22, 79, 22, 87, 22, 22

13. 95, 87, 65, 94, 78, 95

14. 8, 2, 5, 4, 7, 2, 3, 6, 1

15. 89, 7, 11, 89, 17, 56

16. 15, 48, 52, 41, 8, 48

17. 22, 45, 48, 12, 22, 41, 22

18. 62, 44, 78, 62, 54, 44, 62

19. 54, 22, 54, 78, 22, 78, 22

20. 14, 17, 33, 21, 33, 17, 33

21. 65, 51, 8, 21, 8, 65, 70, 8

22. 17, 24, 13, 8, 11, 8, 15, 9

23. 51, 45, 84, 51, 65, 74, 51

24. 8, 74, 65, 15, 9, 10, 74

25. 62, 54, 2, 7, 89, 2, 7, 54, 2

14.6   Scatter Plots

A **scatter plot** is a graph of ordered pairs involving two sets of data. We use these plots to detect whether two sets of data, or variables, are truly related.

In the example to the right, we compare two variables, income and education, to see if they are related or not. Twenty people are interviewed, ages 25 and older, and the results are recorded on the chart.

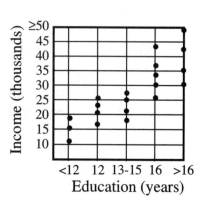

Imagine drawing a line on the scatter plot where half of the points are above the line and half the points are below it. In the plot on the right, you will notice that this line slants upward and to the right. This line direction means there is a **positive** relationship between education and income. In general, for every increase in education, there is a corresponding increase in income.

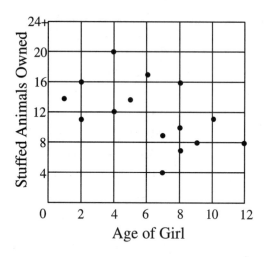

Now, examine the scatter plot on the left. In this case, 15 girls ages 2–12 are interviewed and asked, "How many stuffed animals do you currently have?" If you draw an imaginary line through the middle points, you will notice that the line slants downward and to the right. This plot demonstrates a **negative** relationship between the ages of girls and their stuffed animal ownership. In general, as the girls' ages increase, the number of stuffed animals owned decreases.

Finally, look at the scatter plot shown on the right. In this plot, Rita wants to see the relationship between the temperature in the classroom and the grades she receives on tests she takes at that temperature. As you look to your right, you will notice that the points are distributed all over the graph. Because this plot is not in a pattern, there is no way to draw a line through the middle of the points. This type of point pattern indicates there is no relationship between Rita's grades on tests and the classroom temperature.

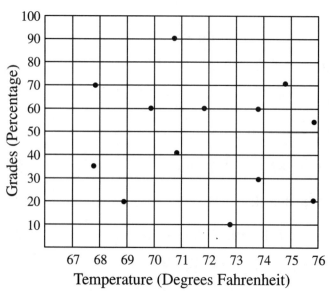

Examine each of the scatter plots below. Write whether the relationship shown between the two variables is "positive", "negative", or "no relationship".

1.

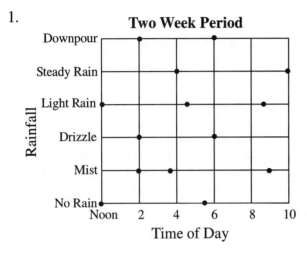

2.

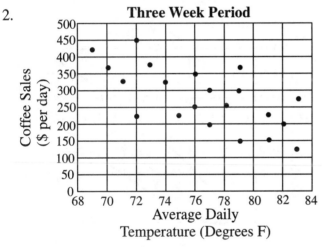

3.

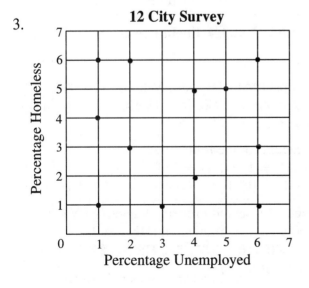

4.

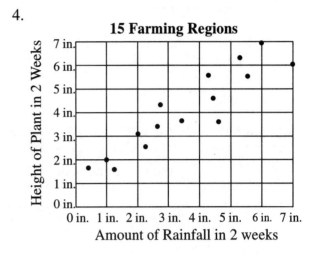

5.

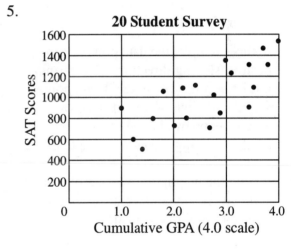

6.

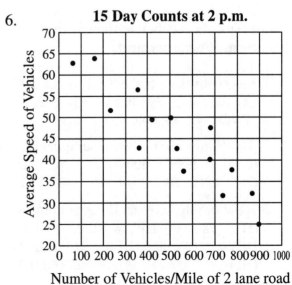

14.7   The Line of Best Fit

At this point, you now understand how to plot points on a Cartesian plane. You also understand how to find the data trend on a Cartesian plane. These skills are necessary to accomplish the next task, determining the line of best fit.

In order to find the line of best fit, you must first draw a scatter plot of all data points. Once this is accomplished, draw an oval around all of the points plotted. Draw a line through the points in such a way that the line separates half the points from one another. You may now use this line to answer questions.

Example 7:   The following data set contains the heights of children between 5 and 13 years old. Make a scatter plot and draw the line of best fit to represent the trend. Using the graph, determine the height for a 14-year old child.

Age 5: 4'6", 4'4", 4'5"   Age 8: 4'8", 4'6", 4'7"   Age 11: 5'0", 4'10"
Age 6: 4'7", 4'5", 4'6"   Age 9: 4'9", 4'7", 4'10"   Age 12: 5'1", 4'11", 5'0", 5'3"
Age 7: 4'9", 4'7", 4'6", 4'8" Age 10: 4'9", 4'8", 4' 10"   Age 13: 5'3", 5'2", 5'0", 5'1"

In this example, the data points lie in a positive sloping direction. To determine the line of best fit, we circle all data points, then draw a line of best fit. Half of the points lay below, half above the line of best fit drawn bisecting the narrow length of the oval.

To find the height of a 14-year old, simply continue the line of best fit forward. In this case, the height is 62 inches.

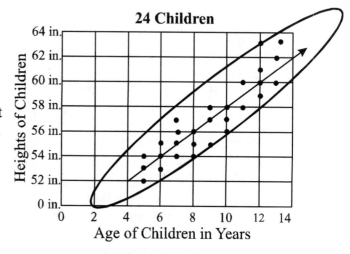

Plot the data sets below, then draw the line of best fit. Next, use the line to estimate the value of the next measurement.

1. Selected values of the Sleekster Brand Light Compact Vehicles: New Vehicle: $13,000.
   1 year old: $12,000, $11,000, $12,500   3 year old: $8,500, $8,000, $9,000   5 year old: ?
   2 year old: $9,000, $10,500, $9,500   4 year old: $7,500, $6,500, $6,000

2. The relationship between string length and kite height for the following kites:
   (L = 500 ft, H = 400 ft) (L = 250 ft, H = 150 ft) (L = 100 ft, H = 75 ft)
   (L = 500 ft, H = 350 ft)(L = 250 ft, H = 200 ft) (L = 100 ft, H = 50ft) (L = 600 ft, H = ?)

3. Relationship between Household Incomes(HI) and Household Property Values (HPV):
   (HI = $30,000, HPV = $100,000) (HI = $45,000, HPV = $120,000) (HI = $60,000,
   HPV = $135,000) (HI = $50,000, HPV = $115,000) (HI = $35,000, HPV = $105,000)
   (HI = $65,000, HPV = $155,000) (HI = $90,000, HPV = ?)

Chapter 14 Review

Find the mean, median, mode, and range for each of the following sets of data. Fill in the table below.

❶ Miles Run by Track Team Members

Jeff	24
Eric	20
Craig	19
Simon	20
Elijah	25
Rich	19
Marcus	20

❷ 1992 SUMMER OLYMPIC GAMES
Gold Medals Won

Unified Team	45	Hungary	11
United States	37	South Korea	12
Germany	33	France	8
China	16	Australia	7
Cuba	14	Japan	3
Spain	13		

❸ Hardware Store Payroll June Week 2

Erica	$280
Dane	$206
Sam	$240
Nancy	$404
Elsie	$210
Gail	$305
David	$280

Data Set Number	Mean	Median	Mode	Range
❶				
❷				
❸				

4. Jenica bowls three games and scores an average of 116 points per game. She scores 105 on her first game and 128 on her second game. What does she score on her third game?

5. Concession stand sales for each game in season are $320, $540, $230, $450, $280, and $580. What is the mean sales per game?

6. Cendrick D'Amitrano works Friday and Saturday delivering pizza. He delivers 8 pizzas on Friday. How many pizzas must he deliver on Saturday to average 11 pizzas per day?

7. Long cooks three Vietnamese dinners that weigh a total of 40 ounces. What is the average weight for each dinner?

8. The Swamp Foxes score an average of 7 points per soccer game. They score 9 points in the first game, 4 points in the second game, and 5 points in the third game. What is their score for their fourth game?

9. Shondra is 66 inches tall, and DeWayne is 72 inches tall. How tall is Michael if the average height of these three students is 77 inches?

On the line below each plot, write whether the relationship shown between the two variables is "positive", "negative", or "no relationship".

10.

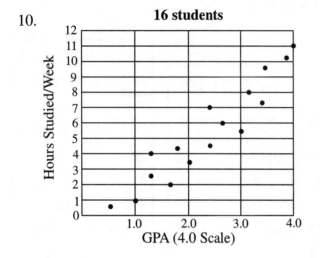

11.

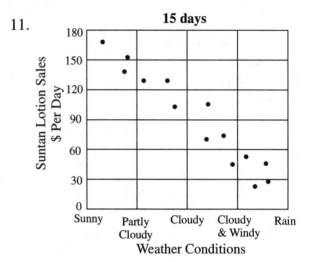

Copyright © American Book Company

Chapter 15
Probability

Probability is the chance something will happen. We express probability as a fraction, a decimal, a percent; or it can also be written out in words

Example 1:   Billy has 3 red marbles, 5 while marbles, and 4 blue marbles on the floor. His cat comes along and batted one marble under the chair. What is the **probability** it is a red marble?

Step 1:   The number of red marbles, 3, will be on top of the fraction.

Step 2:   The total number of marbles, 12, will be on the bottom of the fraction. The answer may be expressed in lowest terms. $\frac{3}{12} = \frac{1}{4}$
Expressed as a decimal, $\frac{1}{4} = .25$, as a percent, $\frac{1}{4} = 25\%$., and written out in words, $\frac{1}{4}$ is one out of four.

Example 2:   Determine the probability that the pointer will stop on a shaded wedge or the number 1.

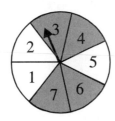

Step 1:   Count the number of possible wedges that the spinner can stop on to satisfy the above problem. There are 5 wedges that satisfy it (4 shaded wedges and one number 1). The top number of the fraction is 5.

Step 2:   Count the total number of wedges, 7. The bottom number of the fraction is 7. The probability that the pointer will stop on a shaded wedge or the number 1 is $\frac{5}{7}$ or five out of seven.

Example 3:   Refer to the spinner in example 2. If the pointer stops on the number 7, what is the probability that it will **not** stop on 7 on the next spin?

Step 1:   Ignore the information that the pointer stopped on the number 7 on the previous spin. The probability of the next spin does not depend on the outcome of the previous spin. Simply find the probability that the spinner will not stop on 7. Remember, if P is the probability of an event occurring, $1 - P$ is the probability of an event not occurring. In this example, the probability of the spinner landing on 7, is $\frac{1}{7}$.

Step 2:   The probability that the spinner will not stop on 7 is $1 - \frac{1}{7}$ which equals $\frac{6}{7}$. The answer is $\frac{6}{7}$ or **six out of seven**.

Find the probability of the following problems. Express the answer as a percent.

1. A computer choses a random number between 1 and 50. What is the probability of you guessing the same number that the computer choses in 1 try?

2. There are 24 candy-coated chocolate pieces in a bag. Eight have defects in the coating that can be seen only with close inspection. What is the probability of pulling out a defective piece without looking?

3. Seven sisters have to choose which day each will wash the dishes. They put equal-sized pieces of paper each labeled with a day of the week in a hat. What is the probability that the first sister who draws will choose a weekend day?

4. For his garden, Clay has a mixture of 12 white corn seeds, 24 yellow corn seeds, and 16 bicolor corn seeds. If he reaches for a seed without looking, what is the probability that Clay will plant a bicolor corn seed first?

5. Mom just got a new department store credit card in the mail. What is the probability that the last digit is an odd number?

6. Alex has a paper bag of cookies that includes 8 chocolate chip, 4 peanut butter, 6 butterscotch chip, and 12 ginger. Without looking, his friend John reaches in the bag for a cookie. What is the probability that the cookie is peanut butter?

7. An umpire at a little league baseball game has 14 balls in his pockets. Five of the balls

are brand A, 6 are brand B, and 3 are brand C. What is the probability that the next ball he throws to the pitcher is a brand C ball?

8. What is the probability that the spinner arrow will land on an even number?

9. The spinner in the problem above stops on a shaded wedge on the first spin and stops on the number 2 on the second spin. What is the probability that it will not stop on a shaded wedge or on the 2 on the third spin?

10. A company is offering 1 grand prize, 3 second place prizes, and 25 third place prizes based on a random drawing of contest entries. If you entered one of the 500 total entries, what is the probability you will win a third place prize?

11. In the contest problem above, what is the probability that you will win the grand prize or a second place prize?

12. A box of a dozen doughnuts has 3 lemon cream-filled, 5 chocolate cream-filled, and 4 vanilla cream-filled . If the doughnuts look identical, what is the probability of picking a lemon cream-filled?

15.1   Compound Independent Events

In mathematics, the outcome of an event may or may not influence the outcome of a second event. If the outcome of one event does not influence the outcome of the second event., these events are **independent.** When someone needs to determine the probability of two events occurring, he or she will need to use an equation.

When finding the probability of two **independent** events, multiply the probability of each favorable outcome together.

Example 4:   One bag of marbles contains 1 white, 1 yellow, 2 blue, and 2 orange marbles. A second bag of marbles contains 2 white, 3 yellow, 1 blue, and 2 orange marbles. What is the probability of drawing a blue marble from each bag?

Solution: Probability of Favorable Outcomes

Bag 1: $\frac{2}{7}$

Bag 2: $\frac{1}{8}$

Probability of blue marbles from each bag: $\frac{2}{7} \times \frac{1}{8} = \frac{2}{56} = \frac{1}{28}$

Example 5:   One bag of marbles contains 3 red, 4 green, 7 black, and 2 yellow marbles. What is the probability of drawing a green marble, removing it from the bag, and then drawing another green marble?

	Favorable Outcomes	Total Possible Outcomes
Draw 1	4	16
Draw 2	3	15
Draw 1× Draw 2	12	240

Answer: $\frac{12}{240}$ or $\frac{1}{20}$

Example 6:   Using the same bag of marbles, what is the probability of drawing a red marble and then drawing a black marble?

	Favorable Outcomes	Total Possible Outcomes
Draw 1	3	16
Draw 2	7	15
Draw 1× Draw 2	21	240

Answer: $\frac{21}{240}$ or $\frac{7}{80}$

HINT: When asked to find the probability of two events that are occurring, there are two key words to look for: "or" and "and." If a problem asks for the probability of one event **or** another event occurring, then you add the probabilities of the two events together. If a problem asks for the probability of one event **and** another event occurring, then you multiply the probabilities of the two events together. You multiply because the chance of having two different events happen is less than the chance of only one event happening, and when you multiply two fractions, you always get a smaller fraction.

Find the probability of the following problems. Express the answer as a fraction.

1. Prithi has two boxes. Box 1 contains 3 red, 2 silver, 4 gold, and 2 blue combs. She also has a second box containing 1 black and 1 clear brush. What is the probability that Prithi selected a red brush from box 1 and a black brush from box 2?

2. Terrell cast his line into a pond containing 7 catfish, 8 bream, 3 trout, and 6 northern pike. He immediately caught a bream. What are the chances that Terrell will catches a second bream when he casts his line?

3. Gloria Quintero enters a contest in which the person who draws his or her initials out of a box containing all 26 letters of the alphabet wins the grand prize. Gloria reaches in and draws a "G", keeps it, then draws another letter. What is the probability that Gloria will next draw a "Q"?

4. Steve Marduke has two spinners in front of him. The first one is numbered $1 - 6$, and the second is numbered $1 - 3$. If Steve spins each spinner once, what is the probability that the first spinner will show an odd number and the second spinner will show a "1"?

5. Carrie McCallister flips a coin twice and gets heads both times. What is the probability that Carrie will get tails the third time she flips the coin?

6. Vince Macaluso is pulling two socks out of a washing machine in the dark. The washing machine contains three tan, one white, and two black socks. If Vince reaches in and pulls the socks out one at a time, what is the probability that Vince will pull out two tan socks in his first two tries?

7. John Salome has a bag containing 2 yellow plums, 2 red plums, and 3 purple plums. What is the probability that he reaches in without looking and pulls out a yellow plum and eats it, and then reaches in again without looking and pulls out a red plum to eat?

8. Artie Drake turns a spinner which is evenly divided into 11 sections numbered $1 - 11$. On the first spin, Artie's pointer lands on "8". What is the probability that the spinner lands on an even number the second time he turns the spinner?

9. Leanne Davis plays a game with a street entertainer. In this game, the vendor places a ball under one of three coconut halves. The vendor shifts the coconut halves so quickly that Leanne can no longer tell which coconut half contains the ball. She selects one and misses. The entertainer then shifts all three around once more and asked Leanne to pick again. What is the probability that Leanne will select the coconut half containing the ball?

10. What is the probability that Jane Robelot reaches into a bag containing 1 daffodil and 2 gladiola bulbs and pulls out a daffodil bulb, and then reaches into a second bag containing 6 tulip, 3 lily, and 2 gladiola bulbs and pulls out a lily bulb?

15.2   More Probability

Example 7:   You have a cube with one number, 1,2,3,4,5 and 6 painted on each face of the cube. What is the probability that if you throw the cube 3 times, you will get the number 2 each time?

If you roll the cube once, you have a 1 in 6 chance of getting the number 2. If you roll the cube a second time, you again have a 1 in 6 chance of getting the number 2. If you roll the cube a third time, you again have a 1 in 6 chance of getting the number 2. The probability of rolling the number 2 three times in a row is:

$$\tfrac{1}{6} \times \tfrac{1}{6} \times \tfrac{1}{6} = \tfrac{1}{216}$$

Find the probability that each of the following events will occur.

There are 10 balls in a box, each with a different digit on it: 0, 1, 2, 3, 4, 5, 6, 7, 8, & 9. A ball is chosen at random and then put back in the box.

1. What is the probability that if you picked out a ball 3 times, you would get number 7 each time?

2. What is the probability you would pick a ball with 5, then 9, and then 3?

3. What is the probability that if you picked out a ball 4 times, you would always get an odd number?

4. A couple has 4 children ages 9, 6, 4, and 1. What is the probability that they are all girls?

There are 26 letters in the alphabet allowing a different letter to be on each of 26 cards. The cards are shuffled. After each card is chosen at random, it is put back in the stack of cards, and the cards are shuffled again.

5. What is the probability that when you pick 3 cards,that you would draw first a "y", then and "e", and then an "s"?

6. What is the probability that you would draw 4 cards and get the letter "z" each time?

7. What is the probability that you draw twice and get a letter in the word "random" both times?

8. If you flipped a coin 3 times, what is the probability you would get heads every time?

9. Marie is clueless about 4 of her multiple-choice answers. The possible answers are A, B, C, D, E, or F. What is the probability that she will guess all four answers correctly?

Chapter 15 Review

1. There are 50 students in the school orchestra in the following sections:

   25   string section
   15   woodwind
   5   percussion
   5   brass

   One student will be chosen at random to present the orchestra director with an award. What is the probability the student will be from the woodwind section?

2. Fluffy's cat treat box contains 6 chicken-flavored treats, 5 beef-flavored treats, and 7 fish-flavored treats. If Fluffy's owner reaches in the box without looking, and chooses one treat, what is the probability that Fluffy will get a chicken-flavored treat?

3. The spinner stops on the number 5 on the first spin. What is the probability that it will not stop on 5 on the second spin?

4. Sherri turns the spinner in 3 times. What is the probability that the pointer always lands on a shaded number?

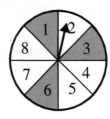

5. Three cakes are sliced into 20 pieces each. Each cake contains 1 gold ring. What is the probability that one person who eats one piece of cake from each of the 3 cakes will find 3 gold rings?

6. Brianna tosses a coin 4 times. What is the probability she gets all tails?

7. A box of a dozen doughnuts has 3 lemon cream-filled, 5 chocolate cream-filled, and 4 vanilla cream-filled. If the doughnuts look identical, what is the probability that if you pick a doughnut at random, it will be chocolate cream-filled?

8. Erica gets a new credit card in the mail. What is the probability that the last four digits are all 5's?

9. There are 26 letters in the alphabet. What is the probability that the first two letters of your new license plate will be your initials?

10. Mary has 4 green mints and 8 while mints the same size in her pocket. If she picks out one, what is the probability it will be green?

Read the following, and answer questions 11–15.

There are 9 slips of paper in a hat, each with a number from 1 to 9. The numbers correspond to a group of students who must answer a question when the number for their group is drawn. Each time a number is drawn, the number is put back in the hat.

11. What is the probability that the number 6 will be drawn twice in a row?

12. What is the probability that the first 5 numbers drawn will be odd numbers?

13. What is the probability that the second, third, and fourth numbers drawn will be even numbers?

14. What is the probability that the first five times a number is drawn it will be the number 5?

FORMULA SHEET

distance = rate × time	$d = rt$
Distance Formula:	$d = \sqrt{(x_2-x_1)^2 + (y_2-y_1)^2}$
Point-Slope Equation:	$y - y_1 = m(x - x_1)$
Pythagorean Theorem:	$a^2 + b^2 = c^2$
Slope Formula:	$m = \frac{y_2-y_1}{x_2-x_1}$
Slope-Intercept Equation:	$y = mx + b$
$\pi = \text{pi} = 3.14 \text{ or } \frac{22}{7}$	

PERIMETER (P) and CIRCUMFERENCE (C)

Any Polygon:	P = sum of side lengths
Rectangle:	$P = 2l + 2w$
Circle:	$C = 2\pi r \text{ or } \pi d$

PLANE FIGURES	AREA (A)
Triangle:	$A = \frac{1}{2}bh$
Rectangle:	$A = lw$
Circle:	$A = \pi r^2$

SOLID FIGURES	VOLUME (V)
Prism:	$V = Bh$ or $V = lwh$
Cube:	$V = s^3$

n	$\sqrt{n}$	n^2
1	1.000	1
2	1.414	4
3	1.732	9
4	2.000	16
5	2.236	25
6	2.449	36
7	2.646	49
8	2.828	64
9	3.000	81
10	3.162	100
11	3.317	121
12	3.464	144
13	3.606	169
14	3.742	196
15	3.873	225
16	4.000	256
17	4.123	289
18	4.243	324
19	4.359	361
20	4.472	400
21	4.583	441
22	4.690	484
23	4.796	529
24	4.899	576
25	5.000	625

ABBREVIATIONS

A = area	l = length
B = area of base	P = perimeter
b = base	r = radius
C = circumference	s = length of side
d = diameter	V = volume
h = height	w = width

Practice Test 1

Part 1

1. Of the 410 visitors at the museum on Saturday, 164 are students. What percent of the visitors are NOT students?

   (A) 30%
   (B) 40%
   (C) 50%
   (D) 60%

2. Tim tosses three nickels on the ground. What is the probability that all three will show "heads"?

   (A) $\dfrac{1}{8}$

   (B) $\dfrac{3}{8}$

   (C) $\dfrac{1}{2}$

   (D) $\dfrac{8}{27}$

3. What is the slope of a line perpendicular to the line passing through the points $(3, 6)$ and $(5, 1)$?

   (A) $-\dfrac{5}{2}$

   (B) $-\dfrac{4}{3}$

   (C) $-\dfrac{3}{4}$

   (D) $\dfrac{2}{5}$

4. Which of the following is a number which, when squared, results in a number less than itself?

   (A) -4
   (B) 4^{-2}
   (C) 4
   (D) $-\dfrac{1}{4}$

5. George has scores of 76, 78, 79, and 67 on four history tests. What is the lowest score George can have on the fifth test to have an average score of 80?

   (A) 85
   (B) 90
   (C) 95
   (D) 100

6. What is the slope of a line parallel to a line having slope $-\dfrac{3}{2}$?

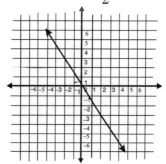

   (A) -6

   (B) $-\frac{3}{2}$

   (C) $-\frac{2}{3}$

   (D) $\frac{2}{3}$

7. Susan rolls three six-sided dice at the same time. What is the probability that all three dice come up 6?

(A) $\dfrac{1}{648}$

(B) $\dfrac{1}{216}$

(C) $\dfrac{1}{72}$

(D) $\dfrac{1}{36}$

8. Lisa's exam scores for history are listed below. What is her average score for the tests?

Test 1	95
Test 2	105
Test 3	80

(A) 91
(B) 92
(C) 100
(D) 93

9. The sum of two numbers is fourteen. The sum of six times the smaller number and two equals four less than the product of three and the larger number. Find the two numbers.

(A) 6 and 8
(B) 5 and 9
(C) 3 and 11
(D) 4 and 10

10. In a basketball shooting contest, which of the following players has the lowest percentage of shots made?

(A) Erica makes 2 out of 7 shots.
(B) Greg makes 60% of his shots.
(C) Bob makes $\dfrac{3}{8}$ of his shots.
(D) Kent makes 5 out of 8 shots.

11. Solve: $\dfrac{3x+6}{-2} > -12$

(A) $x < 24$
(B) $x > 0$
(C) $x > 6$
(D) $x < 6$

12. $(2x)^{-4} =$

(A) $\dfrac{1}{2x^4}$

(B) $\dfrac{1}{16x^4}$

(C) $\dfrac{2}{x^4}$

(D) $2x^{\frac{1}{4}}$

13. Simplify: $\dfrac{(3a^2)^3}{a^3}$

(A) $27a^3$

(B) $\dfrac{9a^6}{a^3}$

(C) $9a^3$

(D) $\dfrac{3a^6}{a^3}$

14. Solve for x:
$2(x+5) + 4(2x-1) = -14$

(A) $x = -2$
(B) $x = -1$
(C) $x = -1\dfrac{4}{5}$
(D) $x = -1\dfrac{2}{10}$

15. Mary owns a cat named Snoopy. She reaches into her bag of 4 fish, 6 liver, 3 chicken-flavored, and 10 milk treats and gives one to Snoopy without looking. What is the probability that Snoopy gets a liver treat?

(A) $\dfrac{1}{6}$

(B) $\dfrac{6}{17}$

(C) $\dfrac{6}{23}$

(D) $\dfrac{1}{23}$

16. What is the slope of the equation graphed below?

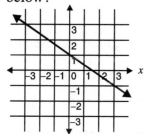

(A) $\frac{2}{3}$

(B) $\frac{3}{2}$

(C) $-\frac{2}{3}$

(D) $-\frac{3}{2}$

17. Solve.

$$7 - \left(\frac{3}{4}\right)^2 =$$

(A) $6\dfrac{1}{4}$

(B) $6\dfrac{7}{16}$

(C) $4\dfrac{3}{4}$

(D) $5\dfrac{1}{2}$

18. Solve: $-6 - x \geq 7$

(A) $x \geq -13$

(B) $x \leq 13$

(C) $x \leq -13$

(D) $x \geq 13$

19. There are three brothers. Fernando is two years older than Pedro. Pedro is two years older than Samuel. Together their ages add up to 63 years. How old is Samuel?

(A) 17

(B) 19

(C) 21

(D) 23

20. Solve $y^2 - 4y - 12 = 0$

(A) $(2, -6)$

(B) $(-2, 6)$

(C) $(3, -4)$

(D) $(-3, 4)$

21. $\sqrt{6}$ is between

(A) 5 and 6

(B) 2 and 3

(C) 4 and 5

(D) 3 and 4

22. Which point on the number line represents -1.2?

(A) P

(B) Q

(C) R

(D) S

23. What is the reciprocal of -52?

(A) $-\dfrac{1}{52}$

(B) $\dfrac{1}{52}$

(C) 26

(D) 52

24. If 60 students eat 24 pizzas, which proportion below may be used to find the number of pizzas required to feed 15 students?

(A) $\dfrac{60}{24} = \dfrac{15}{x}$

(B) $\dfrac{60}{24} = \dfrac{x}{15}$

(C) $\dfrac{60}{15} = \dfrac{x}{24}$

(D) $\dfrac{60}{x} = \dfrac{15}{24}$

25. To make a disinfecting solution, Alana mixes 2 cups of bleach with 5 cups of water. What is the ratio of bleach to the total amount of disinfecting solution?

(A) 2 to 3
(B) 2 to 5
(C) 2 to 7
(D) 2 to 10

26. Translate "eighty-four less the product of six and seven" into an algebraic expression.

(A) $(6 \times 7) - 84$
(B) $(6 \times 7)(-84)$
(C) $84 - (6 \times 7)$
(D) $84 \times (-6 + 7)$

27. Solve: $2(5x - 3) - 6x = 2$

(A) $-\frac{1}{4}$

(B) $\frac{5}{4}$

(C) 1

(D) 2

28. The Rockbottom Blues Band charges a \$300 set up fee plus \$175 per hour (h) that they play. Which statement represents the total cost (c) for hiring the band?

(A) $c = 175 + 300h$
(B) $c = (175 + 300)h$
(C) $c = 300 + 175h$
(D) $c = 300 + 175 + h$

29. Which of these graphs represents $x < -4$ or $x \geq 1$?

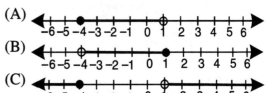

30. The elevation of Port Alice is 10 meters. The elevation of Mount Barbara is 960 meters. It is 100 kilometers from Port Alice to Mount Barbara. Which expression below represents the average increase in elevation (meters per kilometer) from Port Alice to Mount Barbara?

(A) $\dfrac{960}{100 - 10}$

(B) $\dfrac{100 - 10}{960}$

(C) $\dfrac{960 - 10}{100}$

(D) $\dfrac{960 - 100}{10}$

184

31. A racetrack timekeeper records the engine horsepower and top speed of three race cars in the table below.

Engine Horsepower	Top Speed (miles per hour)
140	125
160	130
200	140

Which of these graphs correctly represents the top speed as a linear function of the horsepower of the engine?

(A)

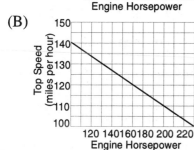

(B)

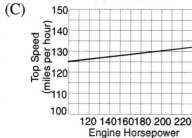

(C)

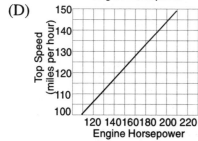

(D)

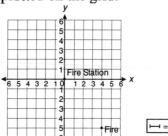

32. Justin records the weights of 6 wrestlers. Their weights, in kilograms, are given below.

66, 97, 52, 53, 76, 105

What is the median weight of the 6 wrestlers?

(A) 52.5 kilograms
(B) 71.0 kilograms
(C) 85.5 kilograms
(D) 86.5 kilograms

33. What transformation of the graph occurs when the graph $y = x - 1$ is changed to $y = 3x - 1$?

(A) The graph shifts down 2 units.
(B) The graph shifts up 2 units.
(C) The slope decreases.
(D) The slope increases.

34. Someone reports a fire at the location plotted on the grid.

How far is the fire from the fire station?

(A) 3 miles
(B) $\sqrt{20}$ miles
(C) $\sqrt{41}$ miles
(D) 9 miles

35. 14.2 is the same as

(A) $\dfrac{142}{100}$

(B) $14\dfrac{1}{50}$

(C) $14\dfrac{1}{5}$

(D) $14\dfrac{1}{10}$

36. If $3x + 4y = 9$, then x equals

(A) $3 - 4y$

(B) $9 - 4y$

(C) $\dfrac{9 + 4y}{3}$

(D) $\dfrac{9 - 4y}{3}$

37. If $x = -3$, find $3x^2 - 5x$

(A) 12

(B) -6

(C) 42

(D) 3

38. Boyle's Law is stated by the formula, $P_1V_1 = P_2V_2$. Find V_1 when $P_1 = 110$, $P_2 = 50$, and $V_2 = 440$

(A) 110

(B) 200

(C) 220

(D) 21, 890

39. Simplify: $4^2 + 8 - 3(8 - 2) + 11$

(A) 237

(B) 137

(C) 17

(D) 42

40. Simplify: $20 \div 2 - 3^2 - (-2)^2$

(A) 24

(B) 16

(C) 5

(D) -3

41. Solve for a: $-4a - 12 = -36$

(A) 6

(B) -6

(C) 12

(D) -12

42. Find $(4y^4 + 2y^2 + 7) + (2y^3 + 5y^2 - 4)$

(A) $4y^4 + 2y^3 + 7y^2 + 3$

(B) $4y^4 + 4y^3 + 5y^2 + 3$

(C) $8y^7 + 10y^4 - 28$

(D) $8y^{12} + 10y^4 + 3$

43. Find $(-3a^2 + 8a - 2) = (-4a^2 - 2a + 6)$

(A) $a^2 + 10a - 8$

(B) $-7a^2 + 6a + 4$

(C) $12a^4 - 16a^2 - 12$

(D) $a^2 + 6a - 8$

44. Find: $(4y^3 - 8y^2 - 5y) - (2y^3 - 5y - 6)$

(A) $2y^3 - 8y^2 - 6$

(B) $2y^3 - 8y^2 - 10y + 6$

(C) $6y^3 - 3y^2 - 10y - 6$

(D) $2y^3 - 8y^2 + 6$

45. Multiply: $(7x^4y^3)(2x^3y^5)$

(A) $14x^{12}y^{15}$

(B) $9x^7y^8$

(C) $9x^{12}y^{15}$

(D) $14x^7y^8$

 **If you want to check your answers to Part 1 questions 1–45 or take a five minute break, you may do so now. After you have checked your answers, continue with the rest of the test. On the Georgia Algebra I End-of-Course Test, you will be able to have a five minute break between each part.**

Part 2

1. Multiply: $(2x^2y)(3xy^3)(-4x^3y^2)$

   (A) $-24x^6y^6$
   (B) $-24x^8y^9$
   (C) $-24x^{27}y^{16}$
   (D) $24x^6y^7$

2. Which of the following is a graph of the inequality $6x - 2 \leq 5x + 5$?

   (A)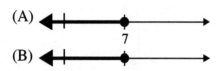
   (B)
   (C)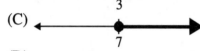
   (D)

3. The graph of which pair of equations below will be collinear?

   (A) $x + 3y = 3$
       $3x + y = 3$
   (B) $x + 3 = y$
       $x - 3 = y$
   (C) $x - 3y = 3$
       $3y - x = -3$
   (D) $3x + 3y = 6$
       $9x - 3y = 6$

4. Wayne takes two markers at random from a box containing 3 red markers, 2 blue markers, and 4 black markers. What is the probability that he will get two red markers?

   (A) $\frac{1}{12}$

   (B) $\frac{1}{9}$

   (C) $\frac{2}{9}$

   (D) $\frac{1}{2}$

5. Which of the following is the graph of the equation $y = x + 2$?

   (A)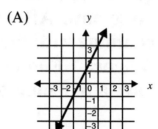

   (B)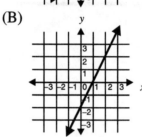

   (C)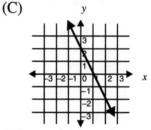

   (D)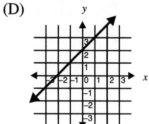

6. Claire wants to divide 58.59 by 6.4 but she forgets to enter the decimal points when she puts the numbers into the calculator. Using estimation, where should Claire put the decimal point?

   (A) 9154.6875
   (B) 915.46875
   (C) 91.546875
   (D) 9.1546875

188

7. Which of the following graphs is not a function?

(A)
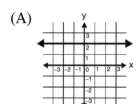

(B)
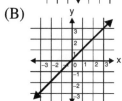

(C)
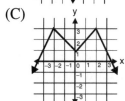

(D)
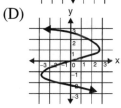

8. Solve: $-\dfrac{6}{x} = 12$

(A) 2

(B) -2

(C) $-\dfrac{1}{2}$

(D) $\dfrac{1}{2}$

9. Jack is four years older than his brother's age, b. Which algebraic expression below represents Jack's age?

(A) $b + 4$
(B) $\frac{1}{2}b + 4$
(C) $4 - 2b$
(D) $b - 4$

10. What is the solution to $2(5-2)^2 - 15 \div 5$?

(A) $-\frac{3}{5}$

(B) $\frac{3}{5}$

(C) 15

(D) $4\frac{1}{5}$

11. What is the slope of the equation graphed below ?

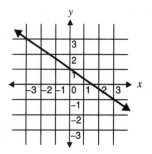

(A) $\frac{2}{3}$

(B) $\frac{3}{2}$

(C) $-\frac{2}{3}$

(D) $-\frac{3}{2}$

12.

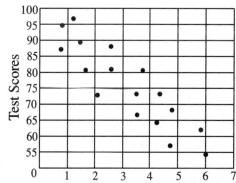

# of hours TV watched daily

Which of the following best describes the relationship in the data points above?

(A) Positive relationship
(B) Negative relationship
(C) No relationship
(D) Cannot be determined

13. Express $\dfrac{\sqrt{12}}{\sqrt{4}}$ in simplest form.

   (A) $\dfrac{2\sqrt{3}}{2}$

   (B) $\sqrt{3}$

   (C) $\dfrac{\sqrt{12}}{2}\dfrac{2\sqrt{3}}{2}$

   (D) $2\sqrt{3}$

14. If Charles spins the spinner pictured below, which of the following is most likely to happen?

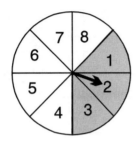

   (A) It will land on an even number.
   (B) It will land on an odd shaded number.
   (C) It will land on an unshaded number.
   (D) It will land on an odd number.

15. Use correct order of operations to evaluate the following expression. $4\left(4x - 3\right)^{2}$

   (A) $16x^2 - 24x + 9$
   (B) $400x^2 - 225$
   (C) $80x - 45$
   (D) $64x^2 - 96x + 36$

16. Simplify the following monomial:
   $5 \times x^4 \times y^5 \times z^{-3} =$

   (A) $\dfrac{5x^4 y^5}{z^3}$

   (B) $\left(5xyz\right)^6$

   (C) $\dfrac{625x^4 y^5}{z^3}$

   (D) $x^{20} y^{25} z^{-15}$

17. Solve for x in the following equation.

$$\frac{6x - 40}{2} = 4$$

   (A) 6
   (B) $\dfrac{32}{6}$
   (C) 8
   (D) $7\frac{1}{3}$

18. Solve for x: $7\left(2x + 6\right) - 4\left(9x + 6\right) < -26$

   (A) $x > -2$
   (B) $x > 2$
   (C) $x < -2$
   (D) $x < -1$

19. Which ordered pair is a solution for the following system of equations?

$$\begin{aligned} -3x + 7y &= 25 \\ 3x + 3y &= -15 \end{aligned}$$

   (A) $(-13, -2)$
   (B) $(-6, 1)$
   (C) $(-3, -2)$
   (D) $(-20, -5)$

20. Simplify

$$\sqrt{45} \times \sqrt{50}$$

   (A) $15\sqrt{10}$
   (B) $\sqrt{2,250}$
   (C) $15\sqrt{2}$
   (D) $\sqrt{9} \times \sqrt{10}$

21. If the equation below were graphed, which of the following points would lie on the line?

$$4x + 7y = 56$$

   (A) $(7, 4)$
   (B) $(0, 14)$
   (C) $(8, 0)$
   (D) $(4, 7)$

22. Five friends study together for the math test. They get an average of 87% on the test. April scores 92%, Alicia has 79%. Monica earns 88%, and Dani gets 90%.What is Elaine's score?

(A) 85%
(B) 86%
(C) 87%
(D) 88%

23. Multiply and simplify:

$$(3x + 2)(x - 4)$$

(A) $3x^2 - 10x - 8$
(B) $3x^2 + 5x - 8$
(C) $3x^2 + 5x - 6$
(D) $8x^2 - 2$

24. Solve the equations

$$-2x - 4y = -14$$
$$5x + y = -1$$

by substitution.

(A) $(-1, 4)$
(B) $(5, 1)$
(C) $(10, -11)$
(D) $(3, 2)$

25. Which of the following is a graph of the inequality $-y \geq 2$?

(A)
(C)
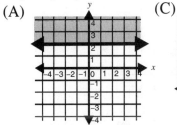
(B)
(D)
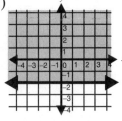

26. Solve the equation

$$\sqrt{6w - 8} = w$$

(A) $w = 3, 4$
(B) $w = 2, 4$
(C) $w = 3\sqrt{2}, 4$
(D) $w = 2\sqrt{3}, -2\sqrt{3}$

27. Find: $(y^3 - 18y^2 - 5y) - (2y^2 - 5y + 5)$

(A) $y^3 - 20y^2 + 5$
(B) $y^3 - 20y^2 - 10y - 5$
(C) $3y^3 - 16y^2 - 10y + 5$
(D) $y^3 - 20y^2 - 5$

28. Find the equation of the dotted line perpendicular to the line shown below passing through the point $(2, 1)$.

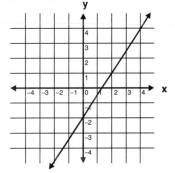

(A) $y = \frac{2}{3}x + \frac{7}{3}$

(B) $y = \frac{3}{2}x + \frac{4}{3}$

(C) $y = -\frac{2}{3}x + \frac{7}{3}$

(D) $y = \frac{3}{2}x + \frac{5}{2}$

29. Construction workers fit a utility pole with a guy wire. One end of the wire is attached at ground level, 8 feet from the base of the pole. The other end is attached to the pole, 15 feet above ground level. What is the length of the wire?

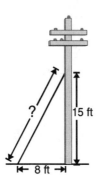

(A) 17 feet
(B) 18 feet
(C) 19 feet
(D) 20 feet

30. Solve the equation $d^2 - 4d + 1 = 0$ by completing the square.

(A) $d = -3, -1$
(B) $d = \sqrt{3}, 2\sqrt{3}$
(C) $d = 2 - \sqrt{3}, \sqrt{3} + 2$
(D) $d = 2i, -2i$

31. Solve the equation $(x - 3)^2 = 1$.

(A) $x = 3, -3$
(B) $x = 1, 3$
(C) $x = 2, 4$
(D) $x = 1, -1$

32. Which of the following computations will result in an irrational number?

(A) $1\frac{1}{8} \times \frac{3}{4}$
(B) $7\sqrt{2}$
(C) $7.2 - 3.1$
(D) 6×3.25

33. What is the slope of the equation?

$$3x - 3y = 5$$

(A) -1
(B) 3
(C) -3
(D) 1

34. Which is the graph of $2x - y = 1$?

(A)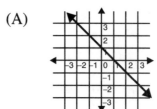

(B)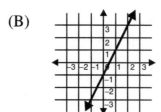

(C)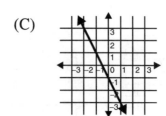

(D)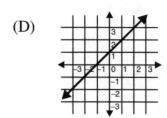

35. Identify the graph of the following function:

$$y = x^2 - 2$$

(A)

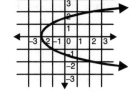

(B)

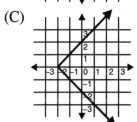

(C)

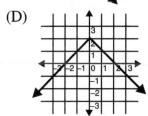

(D)

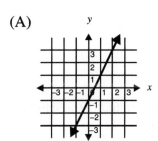

36. $-|-8| - |-2| =$

(A) 10
(B) -10
(C) 6
(D) -6

37. If $c = 5$ and $d = 3$, evaluate $c^2 - 3d$

(A) 1
(B) 14
(C) 16
(D) 19

38. Which of the following algebraic expressions corresponds to: "the product of 5 and x divided by 3 fewer than y?"

(A) $\dfrac{5x}{y - 3}$

(B) $\dfrac{5}{x(y - 3)}$

(C) $\dfrac{5x}{3 - y}$

(D) $\dfrac{5x}{y + 3}$

39. Which is the graph of $-2x - 2y = -2$?

(A)

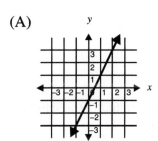

(B)

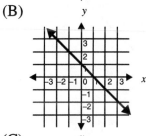

(C)

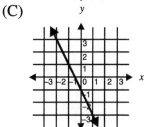

(D)

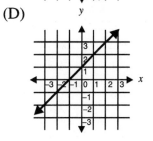

40. What is the equation of the line that includes the point $(3, -1)$ and has a slope of 2?

(A) $y = -2x - 7$
(B) $y = -2x - 2$
(C) $y = -2x + 7$
(D) $y = 2x - 7$

41. Doug buys oak spindle chairs wholesale by purchasing 42 of them for $1,680.00. To sell the chairs at a profit, Doug sells them in dining room sets of six with a solid oak table. Which formula will calculate Doug's cost for the chairs, x, in each dining room set?

(A) $42x = \$1,680$
(B) $\dfrac{\$1,680}{6} = x$
(C) $\dfrac{42}{6}x = \$1,680$
(D) $6x = \dfrac{\$1,680}{42}$

42. In the triangle below, what is the length of side x?

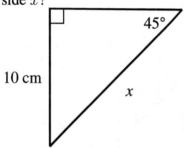

(A) 12 cm
(B) $10\sqrt{2}$ cm
(C) 14 cm
(D) $2\sqrt{10}$ cm

43. Nicole works as an assistant pharmacist. She is paid $9.40 per hour for the first 40 hours per week with time-and-a-half for overtime. Which equation would be used to determine her salary (s) where r is her regular hours, and v is her overtime hours work?

(A) $s = \$9.40(r + v) + .5v$
(B) $s = \$9.40r + 1.5(\$9.40)v$
(C) $s = 40r + 1.5(\$9.40)v$
(D) $s = 40r + 1.5v$

44. Find the value of x.

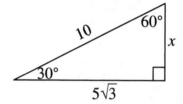

(A) 10
(B) $\dfrac{5\sqrt{3}}{2}$
(C) 5
(D) 15

45. If $2a + b = 13$, then $a =$

(A) $13 - b$
(B) $\dfrac{13 - b}{2}$
(C) $\dfrac{b - 13}{2}$
(D) $2(13 - b)$

194　　　Copyright ©American Book Company

Practice Test 2

Part 1

1. Megan calculates that the diagonal of a rectangular table top is $\sqrt{80}$ inches. What is $\sqrt{80}$ in simplest form?

   (A) $4\sqrt{5}$
   (B) $2\sqrt{10}$
   (C) $2\sqrt{20}$
   (D) 40

2. Della is renting a car for the day. The rental fee (y) is $30 plus $0.25 per mile (m). Which of the following equations represents this cost?

   (A) $y = 0.30m + 25$
   (B) $y = 30m + 0.25$
   (C) $y = 0.25m + 30$
   (D) $y = m(0.25 + 30)$

3. $4^{-2} \times 2^{-3}$

   (A) -48

   (B) $\dfrac{1}{128}$

   (C) $\dfrac{1}{48}$

   (D) $\dfrac{3}{36}$

4. Four students attempt to simplify a mathematical expression. They have four different answers. Which of the answers below is equivalent to the expression, $2(a + 3b) - 4(3a - b) - (5a + 4b)$?

   (A) $-15a + 6b$
   (B) $-17a + 9b$
   (C) $-9a - 2b$
   (D) $-9a + 9b$

5. Susan and Jane are going shopping. Susan has $30 less than Jane. Which of the following could NOT be the amount of money Jane has?

   (A) $20
   (B) $40
   (C) $80
   (D) $160

6. Ryan is dieting. He has plotted his weight on the first of each month for the past 5 months on the graph below.

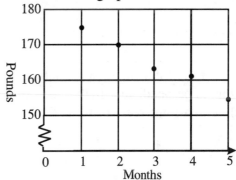

   The slope of a straight line most nearly representing Ryan's weight as a function of month number would be approximately

   (A) -10

   (B) -5

   (C) $-\dfrac{1}{2}$

   (D) $\dfrac{1}{2}$

7. The monthly incomes of 5 individuals are shown below:

$2,540; $9,985; $2,789; $2,748; $2,065

Which of the following best represents the approximate difference between the mean and the median of these five monthly incomes?

(A) $1,200
(B) $1,300
(C) $1,900
(D) $2,700

8. A box of candy contains 3 chocolate mint, 5 chocolate nut, 4 taffy, 6 butterscotch, and 2 vanilla candies. If one piece of candy is selected at random, what is the probability that it will contain chocolate?

(A) 0.15
(B) 0.25
(C) 0.4
(D) 0.5

9. Which of the following is an equation of a line that is perpendicular to the line l in the graph with a y-intercept of $(0, 2)$?

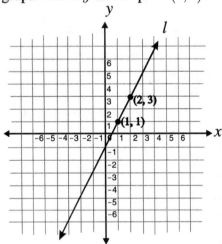

(A) $x - 2y = -4$
(B) $x - 2y = 4$
(C) $x + 2y = 4$
(D) $2x + y = 4$

10. Use correct order of operations to evaluate the following expression.
$-3(x - 5)^2$

(A) $-3x^2 - 10x + 25$
(B) $x^2 - 10x + 25$
(C) $3x^2 - 30x + 75$
(D) $-3x^2 + 30x - 75$

11. Hannah earns 12% commission on any jewelry sales she makes. About how much is her commission on a $45 sale?

(A) $5.40
(B) $33.00
(C) $3.75
(D) $12.00

12. $\sqrt{77}$ lies between

(A) 7 and 8
(B) 8 and 9
(C) 76 and 78
(D) 5 and 6

13. It is $-3°$ outside right now, and tonight the temperature is expected to drop another $21°$. How cold is it expected to get?

(A) $-24°$
(B) $-21°$
(C) $-18°$
(D) $18°$

14. Simplify the following monomial.
$2 \cdot x^4 \cdot y^6 \cdot x^{-4}$

(A) $2y^6$
(B) $2(xy)^6$
(C) $64y^6$
(D) $2x^{-8}y^6$

15. Peter buys T-shirts wholesale by purchasing 125 of them for $250. To sell the shirts at a profit, Peter sells them with his own designs in sets of five. Which formula will calculate Peter's cost, x, for the shirts in each set?

(A) $\dfrac{5}{125}x = \$250$

(B) $\dfrac{\$250}{5} = x$

(C) $x = 5\left(\dfrac{\$250}{125}\right)$

(D) $125x = \$250$

16. There are ten balls numbered 1 to 10 in a paper bag. Amanda picks out a ball without looking and then puts it back and mixes up the balls. If she does this 3 times, what is the probability that she will pick the number 4 each time?

(A) $\dfrac{1}{10}$

(B) $\dfrac{1}{30}$

(C) $\dfrac{1}{100}$

(D) $\dfrac{1}{1000}$

17. Solve for x in the following equation.
$$\dfrac{6x - 19}{-2} = 3.5$$

(A) 12
(B) $\dfrac{13}{3}$
(C) 2
(D) 4

18. $14(x - 6) = -26$

(A) $x = 58$
(B) $x = 4\frac{1}{7}$
(C) $x = -7\frac{6}{7}$
(D) $x = 29$

19. Consider the four sets of data below. Which set has a median of 5?

(A) $\{1, 2, 4, 5, 6, 7, 7\}$
(B) $\{2, 3, 5, 7, 10, 10, 12\}$
(C) $\{0, 1, 3, 4, 7, 8, 9\}$
(D) $\{1, 3, 3, 4, 5, 6, 9\}$

20. The illustration below shows the function $f(x) = 3x - 1$.

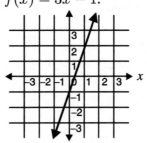

Which graph below shows the function $f(x) = -3x - 1$?

(A)
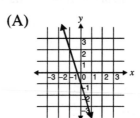

(B)
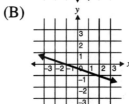

(C)
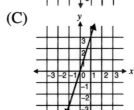

(D)
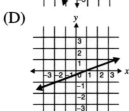

21. Which of the following best describes the relationship in the data points below?

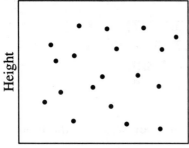

Grade Point Average

(A) No relationship
(B) Cannot be determined
(C) Negative
(D) Positive

22. This year, $\frac{7}{8}$ of all graduating seniors have signed up to go to the graduation dance. What percent of the seniors will be going to the dance?

(A) 0.78%
(B) 0.875%
(C) 8.75%
(D) 87.5%

23. Solve: $3(5x + 3) + 5(4x - 9) = 34$

(A) $x = 1$
(B) $x = 2$
(C) $x = -1$
(D) $x = -2$

24. Solve $-4(2x + 7) > 3(4x + 5) + 27$

(A) $x > \frac{7}{2}$

(B) $x < \frac{7}{2}$

(C) $x < -\frac{7}{2}$

(D) $x > \frac{1}{4}$

25. If the equation below were graphed, which of the following points would lie on the line?
$x - 7y = 21$

(A) $(7, 3)$
(B) $(0, -3)$
(C) $(14, 0)$
(D) $(-3, 14)$

26. Five students receive an average of 84% on a test. Billy scores 68%, Mandy has 92%, Jeanette earns 74%, and Dane gets 97%. What was Stephano's score?

(A) 85%
(B) 89%
(C) 87%
(D) 88%

27. Celeste earns \$7.00 per hour for the first 40 hours she works this week and time-and-a-half for 5 hours of overtime. Her deductions total \$74.82. Which equation will help Celeste figure her pay?

(A) $40(7) + 5(7 \times .5) - 74.82$
(B) $40(7 + 5) - 74.52$
(C) $45(7) - 74.82$
(D) $7[40 + 5(1.5)] - 74.82$

28. Which is the equivalent multiplication problem for $\frac{3}{4} \div \frac{2}{3}$?

(A) $\frac{4}{3} \times \frac{3}{2}$

(B) $\frac{3}{4} \times \frac{2}{3}$

(C) $\frac{4}{3} \times \frac{2}{3}$

(D) $\frac{3}{4} \times \frac{3}{2}$

198

29. In a family of 4 children, what is the probability that all four will be girls? (Making a tree diagram on your scrap paper can help you determine this.)

(A) $\dfrac{1}{4}$

(B) $\dfrac{1}{8}$

(C) $\dfrac{1}{16}$

(D) $\dfrac{1}{24}$

30. Simplify:
$$\dfrac{(2^3)^2}{(3)^{-1}}$$

(A) $21\dfrac{1}{3}$

(B) 96

(C) 48

(D) 192

31. $-|-6| =$

(A) 6

(B) -6

(C) 36

(D) 16

32. Which point on the number line is closest to $-\sqrt{5}$?

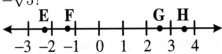

(A) E

(B) F

(C) G

(D) H

33. Solve for x in the following equation.
$$5x + 40 \leq 42$$

(A) $x \geq \dfrac{2}{5}$

(B) $x \geq -\dfrac{2}{5}$

(C) $x \leq \dfrac{2}{5}$

(D) $x \leq -\dfrac{2}{5}$

34. In the right triangle below, what is the value of x?

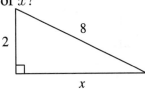

(A) $2\sqrt{15}$

(B) 68

(C) $2\sqrt{17}$

(D) $\sqrt{10}$

35. Find the length of the missing side of the triangle below.

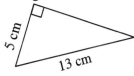

(A) 10 cm

(B) 11 cm

(C) 12 cm

(D) 15 cm

36. Which of the following is the correct solution set for the problem below?
$$21 + 7|a| \geq -14$$

(A) $\{-5, -4, -3, -2, -1, 0, 1, 2, 3, 4, 5\}$
(B) $\{-4, -3, -2, -1, 1, 2, 3, 4\}$
(C) $\{1, 2, 3, 4\}$
(D) $\{-4, -3, -2, -1, 0, 1, 2, 3, 4\}$

37. Find the x- and y- intercept for the following equation: $2x + 5y = 30$

 (A) x-intercept $= 15$
  y-intercept $= 6$
 (B) x-intercept $= 5$
  y-intercept $= 4$
 (C) x-intercept $= 6$
  y-intercept $= 15$
 (D) x-intercept $= 4$
  y-intercept $= 5$

38. What are the x and y intercepts of the equation graphed below?

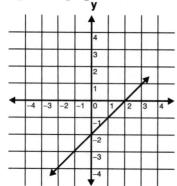

 (A) x-intercept $= 1$
  y-intercept $= -1$
 (B) x-intercept $= -2$
  y-intercept $= 2$
 (C) x-intercept $= -1$
  y-intercept $= 1$
 (D) x-intercept $= 2$
  y-intercept $= -2$

39. The graph of which pair of equations below will be parallel?

 (A) $x + 4y = 3$
  $3x + 4y = 3$
 (B) $x - 4y = 3$
  $4y - x = -3$
 (C) $2x - 8 = 2y$
  $2x + 8 = 2y$
 (D) $6x + 6 = 6y$
  $11x - 12 = 7y$

40. Which ordered pair is a solution for the following system of equations?
  $-3x + 7y = 25$
  $3x + 3y = -15$
 (A) $(-13, -2)$
 (B) $(-6, 1)$
 (C) $(-3, -2)$
 (D) $(-20, -5)$

41. Which of these is the best estimate of the coordinate of Point Q on the number line?

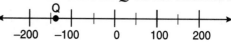

 (A) -140
 (B) -160
 (C) -210
 (D) -260

42. Estimate $7.2027 - 0.5039$

 (A) 6.7
 (B) 7.0
 (C) 7.7
 (D) 12.2

43. Simplify: $3(5x - 2) + (-4x + 5)$

 (A) $4x$
 (B) $4x - 7$
 (C) $11x - 11$
 (D) $11x - 1$

44. Which of these is the equation that generalizes the pattern of the data in the table?

x	f(x)
−3	−5
−1	1
2	10
5	19

 (A) $f(x) = 3x$
 (B) $f(x) = x + 3$
 (C) $f(x) = 2x + 6$
 (D) $f(x) = 3x + 4$

45. Evaluate: $2x^3 - (x^2 + x - 7)$ if $x = -3$.

    (A) -53

    (B) -17

    (C) 49

    (D) 55

If you want to check your answers to Part 1 questions 1–45 or take a five minute break, you may do so now. After you have checked your answers, continue with the rest of the test. On the Georgia Algebra I End-of-Course Test, you will be able to have a five minute break between each part.

Part 2

1. Which of these equations represents, "The cube root of 64 divided by 0.5 equals twice the number n?"

   (A) $64^3 \div 0.5 = n$

   (B) $64^3 \div 0.5 = 2n$

   (C) $\dfrac{\sqrt{64}}{0.5} = 2n$

   (D) $\dfrac{\sqrt[3]{64}}{0.5} = 2n$

2. Solve:
   $$\dfrac{x+4}{2} + 3 = 15$$

   (A) 2

   (B) 20

   (C) 32

   (D) 40

3. Which of these graphs represents the inequality $y \geq 2x + 1$?

   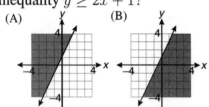

   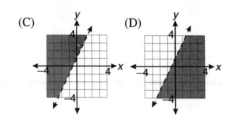

4. Solve:
   $$4(2x - 1) = x - 6(x + 3)$$

   (A) $-\dfrac{14}{13}$

   (B) $\dfrac{7}{13}$

   (C) $\dfrac{2}{3}$

   (D) $\dfrac{4}{3}$

5. Which of these graphs represents $x \leq -1$?

   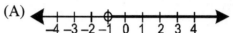

   (A)

   (B)

   (C)

   (D)

6. Which of these graphs represents $y = -\dfrac{1}{3}x - 2$?

   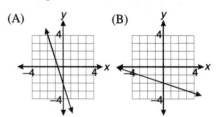

   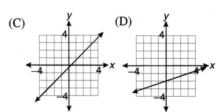

7. A school is installing fiber-optic cable between point m and point n.

   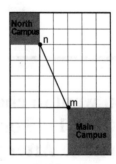

   What is the approximate length of the cable?

   (A) 3.9 km

   (B) 4.5 km

   (C) 4.7 km

   (D) 4.9 km

8. The graph represents the equation $2y = x - 4$.

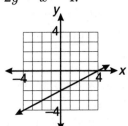

If the coefficient of y changes from 2 to 1, what will the graph look like?

(A) 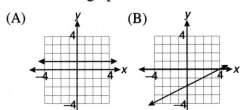   (B)

(C) 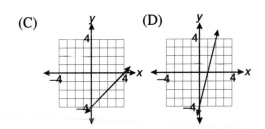   (D)

9. $\sqrt{96} =$

(A) $4\sqrt{6}$
(B) $2^5 \times 3$
(C) $\sqrt{90} + \sqrt{6}$
(D) $96\frac{1}{2}$

10. Simplify: $(5x - 4)(x + 2)$

(A) $5x^2 - 2$
(B) $5x^2 - 8$
(C) $5x^2 + 6x - 8$
(D) $5x^2 - 18x - 8$

11. Solve the inequality $8x - 5 < 12$ for x in the set $\{-2, -1, 0, 1, 2, 3, 4\}$

(A) $x = \{-2, -1, 0, 1, 2\}$
(B) $x = \{-2, -1, 0, 1\}$
(C) $x = \{0, 1, 2, 3, 4\}$
(D) $x = \{-2, -1, 0, 1, 2, 3, 4\}$

12. For the following pair of equations, find the point of intersection (common solution) using the substitution method.
$$3x + 3y = 9$$
$$9y - 3x = 6$$

(A) $(1, 2)$
(B) $\left(\frac{7}{4}, \frac{5}{4}\right)$
(C) $(1, 1)$
(D) $\left(\frac{1}{3}, \frac{1}{6}\right)$

13. Which order of operations should be used to simplify the following expression:
$$6(7 - 2) \div 2 + 5$$

(A) subtract, multiply, divide, add
(B) subtract, add, multiply, divide
(C) add, subtract, multiply, divide
(D) multiply, subtract, divide, add

14. Solve $ab + cd = 20$ for b.

(A) $b = 20 - cda$
(B) $b = \dfrac{20 + cd}{a}$
(C) $b = \dfrac{20 - cd}{a}$
(D) $b = 20cda$

15. Find the equation of the line perpendicular to the line graphed below with the same y-intercept.

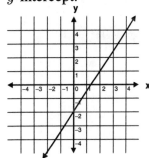

(A) $y = -2x - 2$
(B) $y = -\frac{2}{3}x - 2$
(C) $y = -\frac{3}{2}x + 2$
(D) $y = \frac{2}{3}x - 2$

16. Which graph shows a line with slope $\frac{5}{2}$, passing through the point $(1, -3)$?

(A)
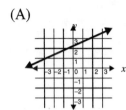

(B)
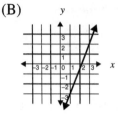

(C)
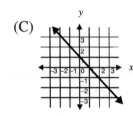

(D)
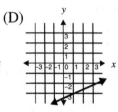

17. Solve $6a^2 + 11a - 10 = 0$, using the quadratic formula.

(A) $\left(-\frac{2}{5}, \frac{3}{2}\right)$

(B) $\left(\frac{2}{5}, \frac{2}{3}\right)$

(C) $\left(-\frac{5}{2}, \frac{2}{3}\right)$

(D) $\left(\frac{5}{2}, \frac{2}{3}\right)$

18. Which equation is non-linear?

(A) $y = \frac{1}{4}x + 2$
(B) $y = -x^2$
(C) $x + 2y = -4$
(D) $2x - 4 = 0$

19. Solve the equation $(x + 9)^2 = 49$

(A) $x = -9, 9$
(B) $x = -9, 7$
(C) $x = -16, -2$
(D) $x = -7, 7$

20. Solve: $1 + 3x - 9 = 4x - 7$

(A) -15
(B) $-\frac{15}{7}$
(C) -1
(D) $-\frac{7}{15}$

21. Shannon has grades of 60, 70, 60, 55, and 68 on her Spanish quizzes. What will happen to the mean, median, and mode of her grades if she gets a 100% on her next quiz?

(A) The mean and median will go up, but the mode will remain the same.
(B) The mean, mode, and median will all remain the same.
(C) The mean, median and mode will all go up.
(D) The mean and mode will go up, but the median will remain the same.

22. Which of the following computations will result in an irrational number?

(A) $8\sqrt{5}$
(B) $1\frac{1}{2} \div \frac{2}{3}$
(C) $2.4 \div 3.1$
(D) $7 + 3.7$

23. Solve the equation $y = \sqrt{16 - 6y}$

(A) $y = 4, 2\sqrt{3}$
(B) $y = 3 - \sqrt{2}, 2 - \sqrt{3}$
(C) $y = 2, -8$
(D) $y = 2 + 3i, 2 - 3i$

24. Solve the equation $c^2 + 3c - 9 = 0$ by completing the square.

(A) $c = 3, -3$
(B) $c = \frac{3}{2}\sqrt{5} - \frac{3}{2}, -\frac{3}{2}\sqrt{5} - \frac{3}{2}$
(C) $c = \pm\sqrt{3}$
(D) $c = 3i, -3i$

25. What is the slope of the equation $-2x^2 + 4y = 7$?

(A) $\frac{1}{2}$
(B) 2
(C) -2
(D) $-\frac{1}{2}$

204

26. Which of the following is a graph of the inequality $x + y \geq 4$?

(A)
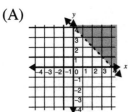

(B)
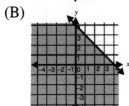

(C)
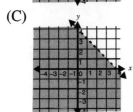

(D)
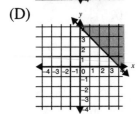

27. Derek earns $212.00 this week. When he gets his check, he finds his employer has deducted 21% for taxes and insurance. How much is his take-home pay?

(A) $44.52
(B) $167.48
(C) $191.00
(D) $212.00

28. Simplify: $3^2 + 4 \times 18 \div 9$

(A) 4
(B) 14
(C) 17
(D) 26

29. Which of the following is a true statement about the relationship between -5 and 5?

(A) $-5 < 5$
(B) $-5 = 5$
(C) $-5 > 5$
(D) $-5 \geq 5$

30. Solve for x in the following equation:
$x + 2(x + 200) + 800 = 3000$

(A) $1,200$
(B) 800
(C) 600
(D) $1,600$

31. At the school store, 5 pens sell for $1.25. Which proportion below will help you find the cost of 12 pens?

(A) $\dfrac{5}{12} = \dfrac{\$1.25}{x}$

(B) $\dfrac{5}{12} = \dfrac{x}{\$1.25}$

(C) $\dfrac{5}{x} = \dfrac{12}{\$1.25}$

(D) $\dfrac{x}{5} = \dfrac{12}{\$1.25}$

32. There are 20 male and 35 female students taking band this year at Washington Middle School. What is the ratio of female students to male students taking band this year?

(A) $\frac{4}{7}$

(B) $\frac{7}{4}$

(C) $\frac{7}{11}$

(D) $\frac{11}{7}$

33. Simplify $4^2 \div 8 \times 2 - 4$

(A) -3
(B) -4
(C) -1
(D) 0

34. Find: $(3y^3 + 5y^2 - 8) + (4y^3 - 6y^2 + 3)$

    (A) $-y^3 + 5y^2 - 6y - 5$
    (B) $7y^3 - y^2 - 5$
    (C) $7y^3 + 11y^2 - 5$
    (D) $-y^3 + 7y^2 - 6$

35. Find: $(2x^3 + 4x^2 + 7x) - (3x^3 - 2x - 5)$

    (A) $-x^3 + 4x^2 + 5x - 5$
    (B) $5x^3 + 4x^2 + 5x - 5$
    (C) $-x^3 + 4x^2 + 9x + 5$
    (D) $5x^3 + 4x^2 + 9x + 5$

36. Multiply: $(4x^2y^4)(3x^3y^2)$

    (A) $7x^5y^6$
    (B) $12x^5y^6$
    (C) $12x^6y^8$
    (D) $7x^6y^8$

37. Multiply: $(-4wx)(-2w^4x^3)$

    (A) $-8w^5x^4$
    (B) $8w^5x^4$
    (C) $-8w^4x^3$
    (D) $8w^4x^4$

38. Multiply: $-6a^3(-2ab^2 + 5a^2b - 6a^3)$

    (A) $12a^3b^2 - 30a^6 + 36a^9$
    (B) $12a^4b^2 - 30a^5b + 36a^6$
    (C) $-12a^3b^2 + 30a^6 - 36a^9$
    (D) $-12a^4b^2 + 30a^5b - 36a^6$

39. Solve: $10 + 3(2x - 6) \leq 4(7 + 2x)$

    (A) $x \geq -36$
    (B) $x \leq -\dfrac{9}{7}$
    (C) $x \leq -18$
    (D) $x \geq -18$

40. Solve: $-\frac{4}{5}x \geq 8$

    (A) $x \geq 10$
    (B) $x \geq 5$
    (C) $x \leq -10$
    (D) $x \geq 10$

41. Factor: $b^2 - 2b - 8$

    (A) $(b - 4)(b + 4)$
    (B) $(b - 2)(b + 4)$
    (C) $(b + 2)(b - 4)$
    (D) $(b - 2)(b - 2)$

42. Which ordered pair is a solution for the following system of equations?
$5x + 7y = -15$
$4x - 6y = 46$

    (A) $(4, -5)$
    (B) $(-3, 0)$
    (C) $(5, -5)$
    (D) $(-1, -7)$

43. Which of the following relations is a function?

    (A) $\{(-2, 2)(-2, 1)(0, 0)(-1, -1)\}$
    (B) $\{(4, 9), (2, 8)(3, 7)(6, 5)\}$
    (C) $\{(1, 5)(1, 4)(1, 3)(1, 2)\}$
    (D) $\{(0, 1)(2, 4)(2, 6)(3, 9)\}$

44. Bryan has test scores of 88, 72, 90, and 82. What does he need to get on his next test if he wants an 85 average?

    (A) 85
    (B) 88
    (C) 100
    (D) 93

45. In Soggy Bottom, it rained 219 of the 365 days last year. What percent of the days did it rain last year?

    (A) 60%
    (B) 70%
    (C) 75%
    (D) 80%

Index

Absolute value, 17
  multiplying and dividing, 18
Addition
  of polynomials, 90
Algebra
  multi-step problems, 79
  one-step problems with addition and subtraction, 64
  one-step problems with multiplication and division, 65
  two step problems, 73
    with fractions, 74
  vocabulary, 50
  word problems, 52
    setting up, 54
Associative Property of Addition, 30
Associative Property of Multiplication, 30

Base, 50
Binomials, 88, 102
  multiplication
    FOIL method, 95

Cartesian plane, 46, 120, 122, 140
Coefficient, 50
  leading, 50
Collinear lines, 146
Combining like terms, 76
Commutative Property of Addition, 30
Commutative Property of Multiplication, 30
Completing the Square, 115
Constant, 50

Decimals
  changing to percents, 36
Degree, 50
Denominator, 19, 28, 93
  rationalizing, 76
Diagnostic Test, 1
  Questions and Topics, viii

Difference of Two Squares, 112
Direct and indirect variation, 61
Distributive Property, 30
Domain, 154, 158

Equations
  finding using two points or a point and slope, 129
  linear, 120
  linear systems
    solving by adding or subtracting, 150
    solving by substitution, 148
    solving systems of equations, 146
  of perpendicular lines, 132
  solving with absolute values, 84
  solving with like terms, 77
  writing from data, 134
Estimated Solutions, 20
Exponents, 23, 88
  division with, 25
  multiplication using, 24
  multiplying polynomials, 91
  of polynomials, 89
  simpifying binomial expressions, 96
  when subtracting polynomials, 90

Factoring
  by grouping, 101
  difference of two squares, 106
  of polynomials, 98
  quadratic equations, 111
  trinomials, 102
  trinomials with two variables, 105
FOIL method, 95, 101, 102
  for multiplying binomials, *see* Binomials
Fractions
  adding, 32
  changing to decimals, 35
  changing to percents, 37
  comparing the relative magnitude of, 34

dividing, 34
  improper, 43
  multiplying, 33
Functions, 158
  recognizing, 159

Graphing
  a line knowing a point and slope, 128
  fractional values, 41
  horizontal and vertical lines, 122
  inequalities, 68, 140
  linear data, 135
  linear equations, 120
  non-linear equations, 139
  on a number line, 41
  systems of inequalities, 152
Greatest common factor, 98–100

Identity Property of Addition, 30
Identity Property of Multiplication, 30
Independent Events, 175
Inequalities
  graphing, 68
  graphing systems of, 152
  multi-step, 82
  solution sets, 69
  solving by addition and subtraction, 69
  solving by multiplication and division, 70
  solving with absolute values, 84
  systems of, 146
Inequality, 50
Integers, 17, 91
Intercepts of a line, 123
Intersecting lines, 146, 148
Inverse Property of Addition, 30
Inverse Property of Multiplication, 30
Irrational numbers, 16

Linear equation, 120, 126
Lines
  collinear
      coinciding, 146
    intersecting, 146–148
    of best fit, 170

  parallel, 146

Mean, 164
Median, 166
Mode, 167
Monomials, 88
  adding and subtracting, 88
  multiplying, 91
  multiplying by polynomials, 92
Multi-Step Algebra Problems, 79

Negative numbers
  multiplying and dividing with, 66
Number line, 41
  vertical, 45
Numerator, 19

One-Step Algebra Problems
  addition and subtraction, 64
  multiplication and division, 65
Order of operations, 18
Ordered pair, 46, 120, 154
  identifying, 47
Origin, 46

Parabola, 139
Parallel lines, 146
Parentheses, removing and simplifying
  polynomials, 94
Percents
  changing to decimals, 36
  changing to fractions, 37
Perfect Squares, 106, 114
Perpendicular lines
  equations of, 132
Point-Slope form of an equation
  $y - y_1 = m(x - x_1)$, 129
Polynomial(s), 88, 98
  adding, 89
  dividing by monomials, 93
  factoring, 98
  multiplying by monomials, 92
  subtracting, 90
Preface, viii

Probability, 173
Product, 98
Proportions, 58
Pythagorean Theorem, 117

Quadratic equation, 110
   $ax^2 + bx + c = 0$, 116
Quadratic formula
   $\dfrac{-b \pm \sqrt{b^2 - 4ac}}{2a}$, 116

Radical Equations, 81
Range, 154, 158, 163
Rational numbers, 16
Rationalizing the Denominator, 76
Ratios, 58
Real numbers, 16
Relations, 154
Relative Magnitude of Numbers, 38
Right triangle, 117

Scatter plot, 168
Sentence, 50
Slope, 126, 146
  changing the slope of a line, 130
  $m = \dfrac{y_2 - y_1}{x_2 - x_1}$, 124
Slope intercept form of a line
  $y = mx + b$, 126, 146
Square roots, 26, 28, 43
  adding and subtracting, 26
  dividing, 28
  estimating, 29

multiplying, 27
Statistics, 163
Substitution
  numbers for variables, 51
Subtraction
  of polynomials, 90
Subtrahend, 90

Table of Contents, vii
Term, 50
Trinomials, 88
  factoring, 102
  factoring with two variables, 105
Two Step Algebra Problems, 73
  with fractions, 74

Variable, 50, 78, 88, 89, 91
  coefficient of negative one, 67

Whole numbers, 17
Word Problems
  algebra, 52
    setting up, 54
  changing to algebraic equations, 55
  ratios and proportions, 59

x-axis, 46
x-intercept, 123

y-axis, 46
y-intercept, 123, 146
  changing the intercept of a line, 130